The English Windmill

Union Mill, Cranbrook, Kent

The finest smockmill remaining in this country was built in 1814 by the millwright Humphrey for Henry Dobell. After falling into disuse during the First World War she was put back into operation by Mr. John Russell, who ran her by wind from 1918 to 1953.

In 1958 the S.P.A.B., assisted by the Kent County Council, undertook the restoration of the mill, which was carried out by a Dutch millwright, Mr. C. Bremer.

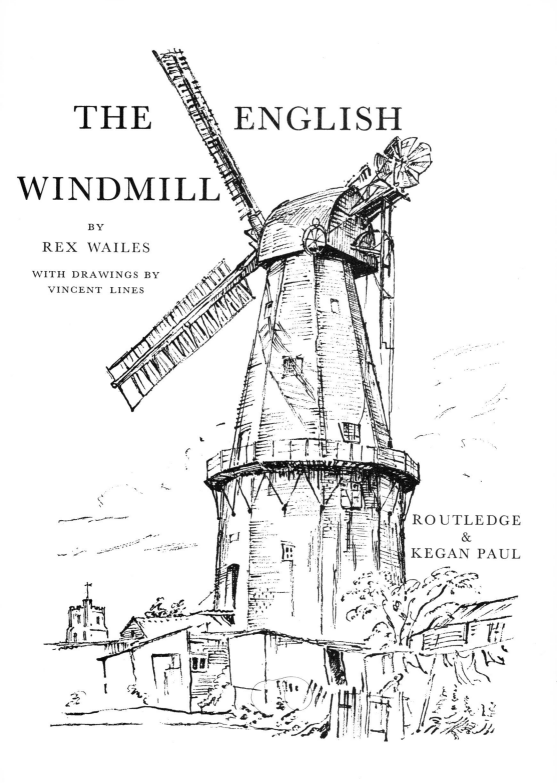

THE ENGLISH

WINDMILL

BY

REX WAILES

WITH DRAWINGS BY
VINCENT LINES

ROUTLEDGE
&
KEGAN PAUL

First published in 1954
by Routledge & Kegan Paul Ltd
39 Store Street
London WC1E 7DD and
Broadway House, Newtown Road
Henley-on-Thames, Oxon. RG9 1EN
Printed in Great Britain by
Lowe & Brydone Printers Ltd
Thetford, Norfolk

Second impression (with corrections and additions) 1967

Reprinted 1971 and 1977

ISBN *0 7100 2241 7*

To
JOHN RUSSELL of CRANBROOK
with
affection and admiration

The windmill is a Couris thing
Completely built by art of man,
To grind the corn for man and beast
That they alike may have a feast.

The mill she is built of wood, iron, and stone,
Therefor she cannot go aloan
Therefore to make the mill to go,
The wind from some part she must blow.

The motison of the mill is swift,
The miller must be very thrift
To jump about and get things ready,
Or else the mill will soon run empty.

Some lines found in a Sussex windmill by M. A. Lower.

Preface

D URING the thirty-one years that I have been carrying out research on windmills, some of the results of which are embodied in this book, I have become indebted to numerous kind friends, acquaintances and correspondents in many parts of the country. So many are they indeed, that their names would fill several pages, and I would ask them, in particular my fellow members of the Newcomen Society, to regard this book as an acknowledgement of my debt to them and also in some measure as their own. Neither must I forget the Press, both local and national, which has been without exception extremely sympathetic to the cause of preserving windmills and recording their history, and the Windmill and Watermill Section of the Society for the Protection of Ancient Buildings for help, which I trust has been mutual, since its inception.

My thanks, too, are due to those who have permitted the reproduction of a number of the illustrations acknowledged on pages xix and xx; to Mr. Vincent Lines, whose drawings are a delight as well as being accurate records; to Mr. Hallam Ashley, who has for many years taken photographs both for me and with me, some of which are reproduced here; to Mrs. Alison Uttley for her kind advice and help; to the Council of the Newcomen Society for permission to quote from the *Transactions*; to Mr. Jesse Wightman for information quoted in Chapter I; to Dr. F. C. Johansen and Mr. John Russell for appendixes A and D, and to Mr. John Salmon and Mr. John A. Clover for the material for appendixes B and C; while I am especially grateful to Mr. Peter Davies for most helpful criticism of the typescript and for reading the proofs.

Finally I must thank friends in the Netherlands, France, Spain and the United States who have enabled me to see their own windmills at first hand and in that way to gain, among other things, a balanced appreciation of The English Windmill.

Contents

Contents

Appendixes

Illustrations

PLATES

xiii

Illustrations

Illustrations

Illustrations

Illustrations

FIGURES

Illustrations

Acknowledgements

PLATES

Plate I is by kind permission of Mrs. Pilcher of Boston.

Plates II, III, IV, VIII and XVII utilise blocks which have illustrated papers of mine both in the *Transactions* of the Newcomen Society, and in the pages of *Engineering*.

Plate VI is by kind permission of Mrs. Price of Margate.

Plate IX is by kind permission of the Officers of the Royal Society.

Plate XII is by kind permission of Mr. B. N. Reckitt of Hull.

Plate XIII. The photograph of Hessle Mill is by kind permission of Mr. G. C. Andrew of South Ferriby Sluice.

Plate XV is by kind permission of the Spalding Gentlemen's Society.

Plate XIX is by kind permission of the National Gallery of Scotland.

Plate XX is by kind permission of Mr. T. B. Paisley, T.D., M.A., of Holywell.

Plate XXII*b* is by kind permission of Mr. Hallam Ashley, F.R.P.S., of Norwich.

Plate XXVIII*b* is by kind permission of Mr. J. Foster Petree of Sutton, Surrey.

FIGURES IN THE TEXT

The drawings of Saxtead Green, Cranbrook, Sibsey and Ashtree Farm Mills are by Mr. Vincent Lines, R.W.S.

Figs. 13, 25, 26, 27, 50, 53, 57 and 58 are by Mr. M. R. Packer.

Figs. 14, 45, 46, 54 and 55 utilise blocks which have illustrated papers of mine in the *Transactions* of the Newcomen Society.

Fig. 37 is from a drawing by Mr. A. Titley and the block is by courtesy of *Milling*.

Acknowledgements

Fig. 43 is by kind permission of the Ancient Monuments Department of the Ministry of Works.

Figs. 45 and 48 and the tailpiece to the book are from drawings by Mr. H. O. Clark.

Fig. 52 is from a drawing by Enid Wailes.

Fig. 61 is by kind permission of the Syndics of the Cambridge University Library.

Figs. 62 and 63 are from drawings by Mr. T. Lewis, M.A., of Spalding.

Introduction

IN these pages I have tried to give as complete a picture as possible of the English windmill, its construction and working, in a way which will, I hope, appeal to the general reader, to those already interested in this and kindred subjects, and to the millers and millwrights whose help and friendship I value so much. For this purpose the book is divided into three parts. In the first, I have described in detail four typical windmills, all of which were at work by wind when Mr. Vincent Lines made his delightful and accurate drawings of them, while the different types and varieties of windmills are also considered. In the second part, I have dealt in technical detail with the component parts of the windmill and I have, as far as possible, quoted examples of actual mills where the features I have described are, or were, to be found. While the first two parts deal mainly with the windmills themselves, the third part is devoted to the purely human approach, and finally there are four appendixes of a specialised nature which are, nevertheless, of very wide interest.

The book is the result of a study covering thirty-one years and one which still continues, although with a rapidly disappearing material to work on. Conclusions have continually been modified as fresh evidence has come to light and isolated facts have fallen into place, linking up others like pieces of a jig-saw puzzle. Much information has died with those who had it; in other instances it has come to light after many years of search.

The attraction of windmills may not at first be obvious, and it must depend a good deal on the windmill herself. For the attraction is individual to each windmill, and in a subtle way is impressed with the personalities of those who have built and worked her. Besides the attraction of seeing a piece of machinery, whose general method of doing the work is fairly obvious, there is the fascination of the defiant challenge to the elements. When one has become aware of the windmill herself there is the appeal to one's curiosity. Who built her and why? What exactly happens inside the mill? And why is so little use made of windmills today?

When you see a windmill, don't think of her as just a pleasant part of the landscape. Think of the thought and devoted craftsmanship that has gone into the designing and building of her, and into her upkeep since then. And to appreciate their value to the full you must experience the fascination of windmills at work. Not only from the outside with the sails moving against the sky as though they were the arms of the giants as Don Quixote supposed them to be, but from the inside too. Inside you hear the swish of the sails as each passes downward in turn; the faster continuous rumble of the gears; the clatter of the vibrating shoe down which the grain is shaken from the hoppers to the stones; the rattle of the sack-hoist chain, and the clap of the trap doors as the miller sends the sacks of grain up to the bin floor at the top of the mill; perhaps the rhythmic tapping of a mill-bill as a man dresses or sharpens a pair of stones; a fine blend of cross rhythms. Maybe the miller is watching and feeling the flow of the meal from the stones and adjusting the feed and the distance between the stones; he keeps an eye on the weather and when necessary he alters the sails to keep the speed of the mill constant by opening or closing the shutters in them like those of a venetian blind. The operations are all supervised by the unofficial foreman—the mill cat; his turn comes when the men are gone.

The English windmill, although doubtless it had its origins on the Continent of Europe, developed in its own way, and while this development must have been influenced by the Dutch drainage engineers of the seventeenth century and visits by English engineers to the Low Countries such as that by Smeaton in the eighteenth century, in the end it was English nineteenth-century practice which spread to north-west Europe, a practice which was based primarily on the art of iron-founding in England. For it was the skill in making accurate castings, both large and small, which made possible the invention of the fantail, with its small gears, the patent sail with its numerous small castings, and the much larger shafts and gears inside the mill itself.

The builders of windmills were the wrights—those who wrought in wood and metals; they were first and foremost craftsmen, and were called later, and more particularly, millwrights. They were the early engineers, and some of the most famous started as millwrights;

Introduction

John Smeaton and Sir William Cubitt are two examples, who were as advanced in their day as our living engineers are in the present age. The work of the millwrights in the mills that remain is part of the history of mechanical engineering, a history that has been as sadly neglected as it is fascinating. They designed and built the horse-mills, the watermills and the windmills. They were masters of many trades, from carpentry and smithing to gearing wheels with wooden cogs and dressing millstones. They mastered the art of 'making do' and nowhere do they show their ingenuity better than in the wind-mill, successfully harnessing a source of power which cannot be controlled.

The millwrights often had advanced ideas. Ball and roller bear-ings were used successfully by them, for certain applications, over two hundred years ago; while spoilers or air brakes were used on sails more than eighty years ago. They arrived by trial and error at a shape for windmill sails, which in the best cases could not be improved upon until the application of aerodynamic principles during the present century. The millwrights were and still are men of considerable force of character, fine craftsmen and as proud of their workmanship as the millers of their mills. Each area had its own tradition in mill-building; that tradition was probably started by one family of millwrights and spread by apprentices who left and started in business on their own.

The study of windmills is by no means a narrow subject, for not only does it cover a wide field, aesthetic, topographical, social, anti-quarian and technical, but I have also been led by it to take more than a passing interest in kindred subjects, to meet people of widely differing interests, and to explore areas which otherwise would have been left unvisited. It has brought me a host of friends and acquaint-ances to whom I owe a great deal of gratitude for their many kind-nesses over the years; and I thank all of them, not forgetting those who have passed on, for the help and encouragement which have resulted in this book.

Beaconsfield, 1954.

PART ONE
The Mills

FIG. I. SAXTEAD GREEN MILL

PART ONE

The Mills

★

I. SAXTEAD GREEN MILL

'The windmills on the hills in the vicinage are so numerous that I counted, whilst standing in one place, no less than seventeen. They are all painted or washed white, the sails are black; it was a fair morning, the wind was brisk, and their twirling altogether added greatly to the beauty of the scene, which, having the broad and beautiful arm of the sea on the one hand, and the fields and meadows, studded with farm houses on the other, appeared to make the most beautiful sight of the kind that I had ever beheld.'—WILLIAM COBBETT, *Rural Rides*, of a prospect near Ipswich, March 1830.

ONE of the loveliest sights I know is that of a windmill at work, the sails turning steadily against a blue sky, with cumulus clouds passing across it in ordered procession. Of all the windmills to see at work I liked best an East Suffolk post mill, tall and white and friendly, waving in greeting as you came to her, waving good-bye as you left her. And of all the East Suffolk post mills the best I ever saw at work was the mill at Saxtead Green (Fig. 1). The setting is its first charm; a large green with small houses scattered round the edges, and on the west side, attended by low outbuildings and a small square mill house, is the mill, white against brown and green fields and blue sky.

The East Suffolk post mills were the finest of their type in the world and Saxtead Green Mill was one of the finest of them. I well remember the kind welcome I got when first I called at the mill more than twenty-five years ago. Mr. Aldred, the owner, showed me over from bottom to top. I met his apprentice, Jesse Wightman, later a

3

millwright and now a farmer, and was finally introduced to Mr. Aldred's family. His mother was then ninety-one. I sat on the steps of the mill ladder beside her in the sun enjoying home-made cake and lemonade; she sent her youngest granddaughter—because she was the youngest—for a moss rose for my button-hole and she told me how once she saved the mill. She was seventy-one at the time, she said, and her son and his man were at Framlingham two miles away, when a sudden storm blew up. The mill, which had been running slowly, was now in danger of grinding up the corn so fast that the stones would run empty and the mill would run away. So unaided the old lady shifted sacks of corn, raised them by means of the wind-operated sack-hoist into the top floor of the mill, and emptied the grain into the storage bins to feed the stones below. Single-handed she ran the mill for a couple of hours until her son's return; for the storm had not touched Framlingham and he knew nothing of it there.

What do we see when we look at the mill from the outside? First the body or buck, as it is called in Suffolk, encased in weatherboards and painted white. The weatherboards on the breast of the mill project beyond those of the sides, those on the sides project beyond those of the tail and those at the bottom of the breast and sides carry down to form a petticoat. Thus protection from the weather driving in is ensured so long as the mill faces square into the wind. Below the buck is the white-painted brick roundhouse with its boarded roof well tarred. In front of the buck are the four white sails and behind it the tall steep ladder and fantail. The buck is mounted on an upright post on top of which it can be turned, and this we can see when we go inside the mill.

Each sail (Fig. 2) has two rows of hinged shutters like the slats of a venetian blind; they are made with wood frames, canvas-covered and painted white. The shutters in each row are connected together by a shutter bar so that all must move at the same time. The shutter bars of all the sails are connected to a four-armed spider coupling at the centre and the coupling is fixed to the front of the striking rod. This rod passes down a hole right through the cast-iron windshaft on which the sails are mounted. Where the striking rod emerges from the tail-end of the windshaft it is attached to a geared iron rack, which engages with a pinion mounted on the same spindle as a chain wheel (Fig. 3). Over this wheel an endless striking chain hangs down to the

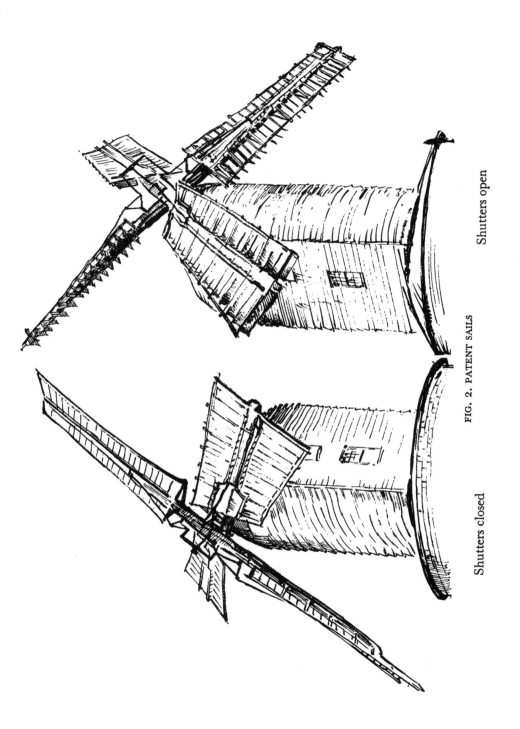

Shutters closed

Shutters open

FIG. 2. PATENT SAILS

platform at the top of the ladder, and by pulling either one side or the other of the chain the striking rod is moved backwards or forwards. As all the shutters are connected to the front of the striking rod they can all be closed or opened at the same time, and either present a working surface to the wind or allow it to blow through them and do no work. This is called spilling the wind and the whole operation can be compared to the opening and closing of an umbrella.

At the tail of the buck is the ladder which you must climb to enter the mill (Fig. 4). The bottom of the ladder is on wheels and above these, on a wooden framework, is the fantail. This turns the mill automatically so that the sails face square into the eye of the wind from whatever direction it may blow. The fantail is itself a small windmill, with its six vanes set at right angles to the sails of the mill. So long as the mill faces square into the wind these vanes only present an edge to it; but should the wind veer it strikes the vanes at an angle and the fantail turns. As it is connected to the wheels at the bottom of the ladder by gearing, these carriage wheels turn also, and move on a level track laid down round the mill, until the mill sails are once more square into the wind. Should the miller wish to turn the mill and there is no wind to do the job for him he uses a large iron handle and turns the wheels through gearing in this way.

The early post mills were much lower and smaller and were pushed round by hand to face the wind by means of a tail pole, which protruded through the ladder at the tail of the mill. They were much shorter too, because sails were plain frameworks over which sailcloths were spread, and this operation had to be carried out from the ground. There is a story, almost a folk tale, for I have heard it told of several mills, which illustrates how close to the ground the sails passed. I first heard it in connection with the second of the two post mills on Brill Common, Bucks, which collapsed some years since.

A travelling tinker with his donkey cart came to the mill one day; the sails were at rest and before going up into the mill to see the miller the tinker tethered his donkey to the lowest mill sail. While he was up inside the mill the wind got up and the sails started to turn. There was a terrible clatter and miller and tinker rushed out of the mill to the top of the ladder in time to see donkey, cart and all lifted off the ground, the pots and pans tumbling out of the cart, and finally the reins break and the whole lot fall to the ground. The cart

FIG. 3. SAXTEAD GREEN MILL

was smashed, the donkey killed, and in all its versions the tale ends 'and people came from miles around to see a dead donkey'.

The tall brick roundhouse at Saxtead Green with its three floors is the same height as the buck, and houses two pairs of stones and other machines driven by an engine. It also protects the substructure of the mill; by this is meant the post, on which the buck turns, and its supporting timbers (Fig. 5). These consist of two heavy horizontal oak beams called crosstrees at right angles to one another, their ends resting on tall brick piers. The post rests on the top of these beams where they cross one another and is quartered over them; that is to say four projections at the four corners of the bottom of the post fit into the four angles formed by the crosstrees. The post takes the whole weight of the buck, but this is not taken by the centre of the crosstrees. Four diagonal struts or quarterbars are mortised into the post just below the bottom floor of the buck and rest on the outer ends of the crosstrees; the weight is thus transferred to the brick piers, on which the crosstrees rest on wood packing but to which they are not fixed. The piers take the whole weight of the mill and post mills are so designed that they are inherently stable on these piers, and this probably accounts for the fact that they have usually been regarded as portable (Figs. 59 and 60).

In the buck at Haughley Mill in Suffolk was inscribed the date of the erection of the mill—November 16, 1811. Mr. Gould, the last man to run the mill, told me that as a boy, he knew an old man who had seen the mill erected when he himself was a boy. A company of soldiers on their way to Harwich to embark for the Peninsular War were resting in the village; they manned the guy ropes and held the post upright while the quarterbars were fixed in position.

Below the bottom floor of the buck are two stout timbers called sheers running fore and aft close to the post, which passes between them; at this point a wooden steady bearing is formed round the post to prevent the buck from swaying about on top of the post as it otherwise would. As we look up at it from the top floor of the roundhouse we notice that there is no top to the sloping boarding of the roundhouse roof; it is not necessary as the buck of the mill covers it, the petticoat of weatherboarding below the buck giving additional protection.

To enter the mill itself you climb the ladder at the tail of the mill, passing under the archway formed by the fantail supports, and

FIG. 4. FANTAIL AND LADDER

mount the steps (Fig. 6). When the mill was in work you were probably preceded by one of the mill cats, scampering on ahead to show you the way and stopping at the top to look round to see why you were so slow. From the platform in front of the door and under the hooded porch you can turn and look at the fantail on the level and note its construction. Each vane is mounted at an angle on a wooden arm, and each arm is socketed into a cast-iron hub; the hub is mounted on a horizontal iron spindle, which turns in bearings on top of the fan spars, as the uprights of the fan carriage are called. Turning

FIG. 5. THE POST AND CROSSTREES

round you find that the door into the mill is in halves; the lower half is shut and pulling it open you enter the mill.

When the mill was at work you were greeted by the warm smell of meal and noticed a fine white dust everywhere. It is surprising how much bigger the mill seems when you are inside; the floor is large and lofty and there is a big sash window on each side lighting it well. On the left-hand side of the floor is a double-flap trap door with leather hinges through which sacks of grain would be raised from the roundhouse below, and in each floor of the roundhouse are four trap doors so that grain could be hoisted up into the mill no matter which way she faced. In front of you is the upper half of the large post (Fig. 7), here sixteen-sided, which comes up through the floor and is capped with a heavy beam which is called the crowntree; this extends

FIG. 6. THE WAY UP

right across the mill from side to side like the top stroke of a **T**. The whole of the framing of the mill is carried by the ends of the crowntree, which is not on the centre line of the mill, but somewhat forward of it. This is so that the weight of the sails may be balanced properly. The top part of the post is cased in an iron casting and above it a cast-iron flange is bolted to the underside of the crowntree.

FIG. 7. THE FIRST FLOOR THROUGH THE DOOR

This latter arrangement is known as the samson-head and it provides an additional bearing on which the crowntree turns; the cast-iron casing is to prevent the post from splitting, as are the wrought-iron bands round the post lower down. On either side of the post are iron tie bars, which tie the crowntree to the two sheers running fore and aft below the floor on either side of the post; there are also two others tying the ends of the crowntree to the bottom of the corner posts in the breast of the mill. All this ironwork has been added at various times since the mill was built to strengthen the structure when it was raised and had the heavy shuttered sails substituted for the lighter cloth spread ones. Let into the floor round the post are four shaped wooden fillets, which are loose and can be raised when the steady bearing is to be greased. In front of the post in the breast of the mill are two wooden meal spouts; these discharge the meal which comes down from the stones on the floor above into sacks, held open by what looks like a horizontal chair leg hung by a looped cord from the framing of the mill, with hooks in it to hold the sack.

Fixed into the framing of the buck are two wooden twist pegs; to these are attached cords which pass through the floor above. These cords controlled the flow of grain to the stones and thus helped to maintain the required degree of fineness in the grinding. The miller felt the meal between his finger and thumb and twisted the pegs, shortening or lengthening the cord according to whether he wanted the meal finer or coarser.

If you look up into the ceiling of the breast of the mill you can see two white squares, with a square hole in each, and an iron spindle passing down through each hole and supported on a wooden beam or bridge tree. The squares are all that can be seen of the undersides of the round bed stones on the stone floor above; they are stationary but the upper or runner stones revolve, and are balanced on the top of the iron stone spindles. The spindles run on footstep bearings mounted on the bridge trees, and these can be raised or lowered slightly to alter the distance between the stones; this is done to maintain the degree of fineness in grinding, whatever the speed of the mill. It was originally done by the miller through a system of levers, and when the wind was steady he could hang a weight on the hand lever or a cord attached to it and be free to do other jobs in the mill. But with a gusty wind he would have to stand by the meal spout and adjust the gap between the stones and the grain feed too, in order to maintain the fineness of the meal. He could of course alter the minimum distance between the stones by means of a screw adjustment.

Some time during the last quarter of the eighteenth century the centrifugal governor was used to regulate the gap between the stones (Fig. 8). It consists of two bob-weights held by suitable linkage to an upright spindle, which as a rule is driven by belt and pulley from some other revolving spindle in the mill. Arms attached to the weights are also fixed to a collar on the governor spindle. When the governor is at rest the weights hang down close to the spindle; but when it revolves they fly outwards by centrifugal force. The faster the mill turns the further out from the spindle the weights fly, and thus cause the collar on the governor-spindle to rise. The collar is con-

FIG. 8. GOVERNORS AND BRIDGE TREE, FIRST FLOOR

nected to the bridge tree, on which the footstep bearing of the stone spindle is supported, by a system of three levers; and as the collar rises the bridge tree, and hence the bearing and the runner stone which has tended to rise with the increase of speed, is lowered but in a much smaller proportion, only a fraction of an inch of movement being required. The automatic adjustment allows the mill to get off in a light breeze and to make the best use of a choppy wind; there is no risk of firing unless the stones are allowed to run empty.

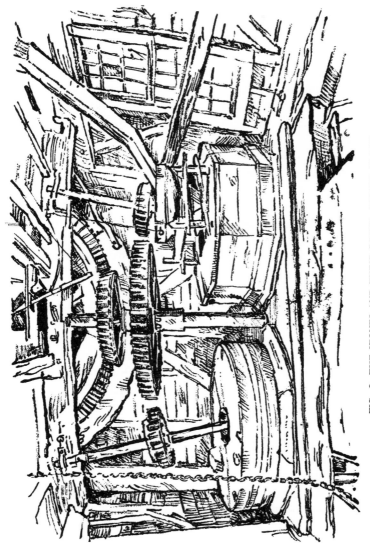

FIG. 9. THE STONES AND THEIR DRIVE, SECOND FLOOR

The Mills

Climb the ladder on the right-hand side to the stone floor above (Fig. 9). Looking forward you can see the stones and their drive, and on the extreme right the heavy brake lever by means of which the brake is applied to stop the mill. Two pairs of stones are placed in the breast of the mill side by side, each enclosed in octagonal wooden stone casings or vats. On a wooden framework or horse on top of these casings are inverted wooden pyramids which are the hoppers. These hold the grain to be ground by the stones and each is fed from the grain bin in the floor above by a wooden spout. The drive for the stones comes from the brake wheel, of which you can see only the lower part and which is mounted on the windshaft which carries the sails. This geared wheel, on which a contracting brake acts to stop the mill, drives an iron bevel wheel or wallower mounted almost at the top of an iron upright shaft. At Hondschoote Mill in the Nord, France, the wallower is of wood with a solid flat top; the miller taught his little dog to jump up on to it while the mill was at work and trot round in the opposite direction to that in which the wallower was turning, so he remained in the same relative position, and he seemed very proud of his trick.

Just below the wallower in Saxtead Green Mill is an iron great spur wheel, and this drives two spur pinions with wooden teeth called stone nuts; each of these nuts is mounted on a vertical iron spindle or quant, the bottom of which is forked. The top or runner stone has a hole called the eye cut through it at the centre, and across the eye is fixed an iron bar firmly cemented in at each end and balanced on top of the stone spindle, which we saw in the ceiling of the floor below. The fork of the quant drives this bar through a coupling called a mace and is the final connection in the transfer of the power of the wind from the sails to the stones.

The top bearings of the quants are bolted to a heavy horizontal tie beam. If only one pair of stones was to be run, an iron strap holding the cap of the bearing was loosened, the top of the quant swung out of the bearing sideways and held in the new position by the strap; one stone nut was then out of gear with the great spur wheel and could not be driven.

The hoppers feeding the stones with grain must not be allowed to run empty and an ingenious device was used to warn the miller; low down inside the hopper a leather strap is placed, fixed at one end to the side of the hopper; a cord fixed to the other end passes through a hole in the hopper, round a pulley and up and over the floor joist overhead, and finally to the trail stick, to which a bell is fixed. So long as there was plenty of corn in the hopper it pressed down on the leather strap and kept the cord taut and the trail stick from falling against the teeth of the wallower. When the corn in the hopper ran low, however, the weight of the trail stick and bell combined caused the stick to fall against the teeth of the wallower. The bell rang and the miller was warned that it was time to fill up the hopper with corn. This device is known as the bell alarm.

FIG. 10. THE TOP FLOOR: A SACK IS HOISTED

The two lower floors of the mill are well lighted by large sash windows on each side; but now we climb the next ladder up to the top floor, which has only a small window in the rear gable. In the early mills, and in a few old ones surviving today, glazed windows were unknown. The mill was lit by openings in the weatherboarding, round or rectangular and closed by wooden shutters, as well as by opening the top half of the door. In Saxtead Green Mill the only shutter is the storm hatch, above the neck of the windshaft and just behind the sails. The roof of the buck is low and curved, the rafters springing from floor level; the floor is mostly taken up with storage bins, the big wooden brake wheel filling the breast. There is a curious arrangement of pulleys and shafts in the top of the roof; this is the sack hoist by means of which the sacks of grain were hoisted up into the top of the mill and emptied into the bins (Fig. 10). Here it was stored and fed to the hoppers of the stones when required.

The sack hoist consists of a wooden shaft in the roof running parallel to the ridge with wooden battens nailed along its length forming a long drum. A chain was fixed to the drum and wound up on it when sacks were raised. This sack chain passes over a pulley in the roof and down through double-flap trap doors into the round-house. The hoist was driven by a wooden pulley fixed to the wind-shaft close to the brake wheel. A belt passes round this pulley and another one on the chain drum of the sack hoist; normally this belt was slack and did not drive the sack hoist while the mill was at work. To work the sack hoist a cord which passes down through all the floors was pulled. This operated a lever with a roller mounted on it which pressed against the slack belt and tightened it; the belt drove the pulley on the chain drum and the chain was wound up on to the drum, hoisting any sack that the miller had hitched to the lower end.

When the sack came through the last trap door in the top floor of the mill the miller let go the cord. The belt became slack again and no longer drove, and the sack was ready for the grain in it to be tipped into the storage bins.

The earliest reference to a sack hoist is contained in a book called *The Life of Long Meg of Westminster*, who fought at the siege of Boulogne and died before 1594. The extract below makes amusing reading.

'Meg going one day with sundry of her neighbours to make merry all afoot because the weather was coole, and it was a great Frost, and none with them but a young stripling of some fourteen years old, for their husbands about businesse were gone another way; it chanced that they went by Epping Mill, where the Miller was looking out, for the wind blew faire and the Sailes went merrily. The little boy, that was a wag, thought to be merry with the Miller, and therefore called to him Miller put out, put out Miller. What shall I put out boy, quoth the Miller? Marry, quoth the boy, a theeuses head, and a theeuses pair of eares, put out Miller, put out. At this the Miller in great rage came running down and beat the boy. Meg stept to him and would have stayed his hand; and the Miller lent her three or four good bangs over the shoulder. Meg felt it smart, and shee got within the Miller wroong the sticks out of his hand, and beswinged him well, and when she had done sent the boy up for an empty sacke, and put the Miller in all but the head, and then tying him in the rope wherewith they pulled the sackes hal'd him halfe way, and there let him hang. Where the poore miller cried out for helpe, and if his wife had not been coming, himselfe had been almost kill'd and

FIG. 11. STONE-DRESSING IN THE TAIL OF THE SECOND FLOOR

the Mill for want of corne set on fire. Thus Meg plagued the sawcie Miller of Epping.'

After grinding for some time mill stones become dulled and have to be sharpened or dressed; to do this it is necessary to raise and turn over the runner stone (Fig. 11). The tip of a crowbar is forced between the stones; a long hardwood wedge is then inserted in the gap and the stones raised with the crowbar until a rope can be passed between the stones and through the eye of the runner stone. The fulcrum for the crowbar is more often than not a piece of stepped hard wood, sometimes called a many-height. In post mills a turn of rope is usually taken round the windshaft, the other end being attached to the stone, which can then be raised by windpower by careful manipulation of the brake. Before dressing, the stones are staffed with a laminated mahogany staff proved on a cast-iron straight edge, scraped up true with glass and smeared with a compound of fat and red iron oxide which is known as raddle. After staffing the stones the high spots are dressed down to the level of the rest of the land, the runner stone is slightly relieved round the eye, and the furrows are dressed; the master furrows running from the eye at the centre to the outer edge, and the others branching off from them.

The instruments used in dressing are steel picks and bills, both double ended—the former pointed, the latter like a chisel—and both are wedged into the heads of wooden thrifts, which bear some slight resemblance to a sculptor's mallet.

Before replacing the runner stone it is necessary to make sure that the stone spindle runs true; to test this a flat piece of wood called a jack, having a hole in one end, is placed over the spindle; a quill is fixed in the other end and adjusted so that it just scratches the surface of the bedstone. The footstep bearing of the stone spindle, the pad of which was often an old cartwheel penny, is adjusted sideways in its housing, which has four set screws and is known as a bridging box, until the quill just scratches evenly round the full circle. One man on the stone floor operated the jack and the other below adjusted the footstep bearing, and plenty of swearing was heard from above when the man below turned the wrong screw. A new runner stone has to be properly balanced before use, the usual method being to run lead into a hole when testing has shown at which point it is lightest.

Stone-dressing, while usually carried out by millers themselves and by millwrights, was sometimes done by itinerant stone-dressers who walked from mill to mill—both wind and water mills—and slept beside their job until it was finished. Anyone who had done much stone-dressing could easily be remarked by the small blue streaks on the backs of his hands; these are caused by flying splinters of steel from the mill bills getting under the skin and remaining there, and before engaging a stone-dresser the miller would often ask him to show his steel as a proof that he was well used to dressing mill stones. I have heard it asserted, however, that a skilled stone-dresser using properly tempered mill bills did not acquire this time-honoured hall-mark. Stone-dressing is a lengthy and tiring job and it has well been

FIG. 12. MR. A. S. ALDRED

said that it takes three years in a mill to learn to dress the stones properly.

In 1950 the Ancient Monuments Department of the Ministry of Works accepted guardianship of Saxtead Green Mill from Mr. and Mrs. Sullivan, son-in-law and daughter of Mr. A. S. Aldred (Fig. 12). Repairs to be carried out will put the mill in first-class order as a landmark, and though she is not likely to work by wind again we now have preserved for the nation one of the finest post mills in the world.

Mr. Jesse Wightman, who knows the mill better than anyone now alive, sent me the following comprehensive information on the history of the mill.

'The earliest date relative to the mill is June 6th, 1796, when it was in the hands of one Amos Webber; who was also a farmer and ground for farmers. Amos Webber was followed by Robert Holmes, George Holmes, William Holmes, Mr. Meadows, a Mr. Eldred, then A. Aldred and A. S. Aldred. It had at that time four common sails and a wooden windshaft, was winded by a tail pole and tiller, and had a collar or yoke on the tail pole for the miller to put his head through when he pushed it round.

'It is doubtful if the mill ever had an open substructure as there is no paint left on the quarterbars. The roundhouse was then approximately 8 or 9 feet high at the wall, and the sails long enough to hit a pig as it walked in the yard. At that time it possibly had only one pair of stones in the centre of the head or breast and the head wheel or brake wheel had 72 cogs about 4 in. pitch. The mill has been lifted on the brickwork three times altogether. Once it was tail-winded standing East or South East and the vanes and bits of sails were thrown across the three cornered piece of green, and perhaps that is when the present windshaft was put in, dated 1854. At some time the right hand side stones had a pair of bevel wheels underneath with a pulley outside for driving off a portable steam engine when there was no wind. Whether the great spur wheel was put in and the mill converted into a two pair mill the last time it was heightened I do not know. It was probably done before, as a belt drive on the back at the present height is almost hopeless, and seeing that an old two-pair steam tackle [1] was in the roundhouse as early as 1872 it seems possible that the top stones were steam driven before the mill

[1] i.e. Two pairs of stones driven by steam engine.

was heightened. A Mr. Meadows had it lifted the last time and that was during the 1850s.

'The first fly tackle [fan tail] had high wheels on the track; these used to jump off the track during a gale and were always a trouble. Mr. A. Aldred got Collins of Melton to put low wheels on with a worm drive on each and these were on till approximately 1922; but they were always slow in motion and drove heavily; the present gear is much better, it came off the old Worlingworth Mill. The stairs or ladder came off Sweffling High Mill about 1912, and this mill had fly on the roof and two tracks, one for stairs and one for tail pole. A new fly and new fly posts were put on about 40 years ago, the old one having been blown to bits one Saturday afternoon. The new track, five yards bigger round, was put down in 1922 by Sam Clarke and the Worlingworth wheels and frame fitted at the same time. Whitmore and Binyon put the cap on the post and the plate under the crowntree for Mr. A. Aldred. A bolter across the tail was driven from a truck wheel [pulley], which drove off a cross shaft with a skew gear from the brake wheel.

'Mr. A. Aldred had two new stocks put up and the old sails thoroughly repaired in 1877 or 78 by Collins and again by Whitmore & Binyon in 1899. Mr. A. S. Aldred put up a new inside stock in 1914 and a secondhand outside stock from Haskerton tower mill in 1925. Then I put up a secondhand inside stock from Peasenhall post mill in 1943. One inside clamp came off Diss smock mill and the other inside clamp off Haskerton Mill. When Collins repaired the four sails in 1877 or '8 a Mr. Tolman, farmer, of Wood Hall, Saxtead, carried them to Melton on a wagon. Now if these were only made in 1854, it seems rather odd that they should be getting "queer" in 23 or 24 years. This, and the steam power to the buck makes me think that they must have been either patent or spring sails. Then again, over against all this, an old man—Noah Goddard—told me he could remember cloth sails on the mill, and Meadows having it heightened. This I was told about 1924 or 1925. The old man was then getting on for 90 years of age. The late Mr. A. S. Aldred told me of one—Philip Bloomfield—an old man when A. S. Aldred was a youth—who used to tell very much the same tale. However, one is safe in saying that the period between cloth sails and the iron shaft, and patent sails could not have been long, and the head of the mill all denotes that the tailwinding episode was rather disastrous. The dwelling house was built for—I think—Robert Holmes, in 1810, and when we cut through a stud-and-plaster wall upstairs, one or two studs were old pieces of sail whip.

'When the mill was converted to patent sails I do not know, but the chain purchase wheel is by Whitmore & Binyon. The first striking gear pushed the spider coupling on the front end of the striking rod outwards, to cloth or close the vanes. The stump irons or posts were cast-iron of T section and were heavy and cumbersome. The triangles were pivoted on to these at the corner of the perpendicular and base. About 1912 or '14 these heavy stump irons were replaced by short ones; the triangles were pivoted at the corner of the base and the hypotenuse and the spider was made to pull in to cloth the mill. The former method needed about 98 lbs. weight on the striking chain, the latter about 35 lbs. The rack and pinion at the tail of the striking rod was formerly of coarse pitch and this was altered to a smaller pinion of finer pitch and a rack to suit; at the same time the shaft carrying the chain purchase wheel was heightened, so that the pinion is now above the rack, whereas before it was underneath it. Thus the direction of rotation of the chain wheel is the same to pull the spider in as it was formerly to push it out.

'About 1942 we altered the pivoting of the triangles over from the base-to-hypotenuse corner, to the base-to-perpendicular corner; the mill worked better in this position than anywhere else and thus they remain. When I repaired Syleham post mill I made the same alteration and the sails strike and regulate in a gusty wind very well.

'As to millwrights, Simon Nunn did some repairs in the 1880's, and we can say that the millwrights have been Collins, then Nunn, then Whitmore & Binyon, then Sam Clarke Senior, then George Clarke, then Sam Clarke junior, and we did the work ourselves from 1926.

'When A. Aldred took Saxtead mill, it had a pair of 4 ft. stones in the breast on the left hand side and a pair of 4 ft. 4 in. wheatstones nearly new on the right; these were smothered with black grease. The left hand pair afterwards were replaced by a pair of 4 ft. wheatstones from the roundhouse and were dressed for grist. In 1917 the bedstone was worn out and replaced by a 4 ft bedstone from Framlingham steam mill and in 1919 the runner was replaced by one from Monewden post mill. The bedstone from Framlingham was replaced in 1931 with one from Eye post mill roundhouse which had previously been brought from Mellis steam mill. The 4 ft. 4 in. stones were there till 1936 when we took them down to lighten the mill and replaced them with a 3 ft. 6 in. runner stone from Snape post mill roundhouse, and a bedstone I built with burrs I got by collecting. Some came from a 4 ft. 10 in. runner from Barley Green post mill, Stradbrooke, some from a 4 ft. 4 in. runner from Ubbeston post mill, others from a 3 ft. 6 in. bedstone off Aldridge's post mill Hunting-field, the rest from a 3 ft. 10 in. runner stone that was steam driven in Hoxne water mill. What a pedigree for a 3 ft. 6 in. bedstone! These are all the stones the windmill has had since it became Aldred's mill. I have no reliable information previous to this.

'Now the stones in the roundhouse when Alfred Aldred took the mill in 1872 were a pair of 4 ft. diameter wheatstones that were put in the mill and converted to grind grist, and another pair of 4 ft. grist stones. The first pair were replaced by a pair of 4 ft. wheatstones which were taken out of Press Bros. flour mill at Yarmouth; the second were replaced by a pair of 4 ft. 8 in. grist stones that came from the old post mill at Redlingfield which was blown down the 18th Jan., 1881. These two pairs were used until after the first oil engine was fixed in 1895. In 1896 a pair of 3 ft. 8 in. wheatstones from Barnham steam mill were put in. In 1895 or early 1896, a pair of 4 ft. stones were bought off Roe of Horham post mill. These were a very hard pair and proved wasters. They were installed because the 4 ft. 8 in. stones were too big for the oil engine. The 4 ft. stones which came from Press Bros., High Mill, Yarmouth (Plate III), were used till the runner wore out in 1928 when it was replaced by a new emery composition runner supplied by William Garner & Sons, Millwall. The bedstone was used till it wore out in 1935 and was replaced by a 4 ft. bedstone that came from Monewden, the fellow to the left hand runner in the windmill. These are all the millstones that have been used in the roundhouse. A. S. Aldred used to say that as a little boy he could remember the 4 ft. 8 in. stones from Redlingfield being unloaded; one slid into the low ground adjoining the ditch, and they had difficulty in getting it back.

'When A. Aldred took the mill the steam tackle drove with iron bevel gears from a lay to an upright shaft. A belt drum and belt drove onto the grist stones, and the wheatstones were driven by a second belt off the grist stone spindle; thus you had to drive the grist stones to drive the wheatstones. These were scrapped, and Whitmore's

installed the present gearing which is bevel and spur. These
have never run smoothly, as the bevel wheels are not a pair and
hence are out of pitch. The left hand crotch spindle or quant in the
windmill is wrought-iron and was put in by Collins of Melton when

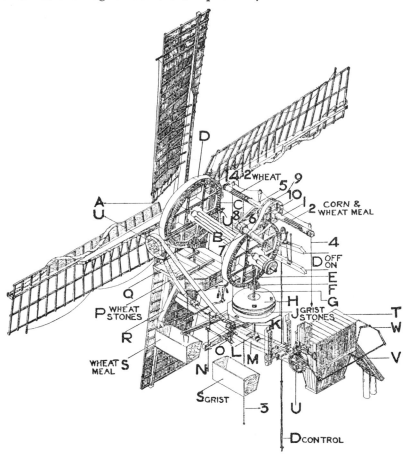

FIG. 13. POST MILL

A, Sail. B, Windshaft. C, Brake wheel. D, Brake. E, Tail wheel. F, Stone nut.
G, Quant. H, Runner stone. J, Bedstone. K, Stone spindle. L, Bridging box.
M, Bridge tree. N, Adjusting screw. O, Governors. P, Stone casing. Q, Hopper.
R, Meal spout. S, Meal bin. T, Wire machine. U, Drive for wire machine.
V, Jog-scry. W, Drive for jog-scry.

1, Sack hoist spindle. 2, Sack hoist drum. 3, Sack hoist chain. 4, Sack hoist
control cord. 5, Sack hoist rocking lever. 6, Sack hoist rocking lever pivot. 7, Sack
hoist drive spindle. 8, Sack hoist drive friction wheel. 9, Sack hoist drive belt.
10, Sack hoist drive pulley.

the old one broke. The right hand quant crotch was cast by Young's of Diss from a pattern I made in the late 1930s.

'The engine shed is the only building that there was with the mill when A. Aldred took it in the early 1870s. An old man, who died in Framlingham 30 years ago and was over 90 years old, was one of the first drivers of old portable steam engines in these parts. He used to speak of threshing during the day and driving various mills at night when there was a long spell of calm. One mill he had driven was Saxtead and for Holmes, but which Holmes I do not know.

'The first engine installed by A. Aldred was an upright bottle engine and proved useless. Then an 8 H.P. portable, by Woods & Co. of Stowmarket, was there until the first oil engine using paraffin was installed. This was a Hornsby-Ackroyd 12 H.P. No. 701 and it was replaced by a Ruston M-type 15 H.P. crude oil engine in 1925.'

II. THE POST MILL

As has been seen from the description of Saxtead Green Mill, the post mill is an ingeniously contrived piece of mechanism and in England it varied considerably according to local tradition. The early mills were very small and had straight pitched roofs and no roundhouse, they were turned to the wind by a tail pole, had cloth spread or common sails, and contained only one pair of stones, situated in the breast of the mill and driven direct from the brake wheel. The oldest post mill of which I have any knowledge stood on the Gosberton Road at Surfleet, Lincolnshire. It worked until 1909 and was pulled down by a traction engine in 1912. An inscription inside read: 'This mill was started in 1509 by G. M. H. Devcal.' [1] The oldest surviving example is Bourn Mill, Cambridgeshire (Figs. 59 and 60), which Major-General Hendly proved to be in existence in 1636, but the date of whose building is unknown. The mill itself is the original, but the machinery inside has been renewed, some of it twice, and the mill body extended at the rear by enclosing the platform at the top of the main ladder. This was quite commonly done in many mills, probably when flour-dressing machines (bolters) were installed, for at one time bolting was done by the mealmen and not

---

[1] *The Lincolnshire, Boston & Spalding Free Press*, 15th October, 1912.

by the millers, while large households had domestic bolters. The mill stones are now regulated by governors, but at one time, of course, this regulation was done by hand, and the shutters in the sides and the window in the breast of the first floor are so placed that standing by the meal spout, feeling the meal and regulating the stones, the miller could see out of them and through the door and so keep an eye on the weather in all quarters. Down one side of the ladder there was sometimes a sack slide (Plate XIV), sometimes fixed but more often hinged, which enabled sacks to be lowered rapidly for loading —and small boys to enjoy themselves. One of the hinged type, which folds sideways at right angles to the ladder, was to be seen at Cross-in-Hand Mill, Sussex. At Keysoe Mill in Bedfordshire and Friskney Tofts Mill in Lincolnshire, both now destroyed, two wind indicators were fitted, each consisting of four small wooden blades revolving horizontally and fitted into opposite walls on the first floor of the mill, there being a horizontal slit in the wall for each indicator to enable the wind to operate it. If both turned, the mill was sufficiently true into the wind, but if one stopped the miller knew that he must turn the mill. These indicators were also to be found in many French post mills all over the country.

The substructures of the post mills have a family likeness but considerable variations can be found. The most obvious was the use of three crosstrees and six quarterbars in place of the usual two and four. This practice, whose purpose seems to have been additional stability, could be seen in mills at Bledlow Ridge, Bucks, and Chinnor and Stokenchurch in Oxfordshire (Plate XXIII), Costock in Nottinghamshire and Moreton in Essex; the latter mill survives, preserved by the Essex County Council. Posts frequently had four additional mortises in between the tops of the quarterbars, which were used for temporary struts to hold the post vertical while the quarterbars were being fitted. As at Saxtead Green Mill, each post had a steady bearing at the point where it passed through the bottom floor of the body formed by the two stout sheers on either side of it, which run fore and aft the full length of the body, and two short trimmers between the sheers fore and aft of the post. In addition, there was sometimes a second framed-up bearing or collar, on top of which the sheers bore so that the mill had both vertical and horizontal bearings to keep the body from swaying about on top of the post. At Sprowston Mill, Norwich, a ball-bearing collar, thought to

The Post Mill

date from 1780, was used. It consisted of two cast-iron rings thirty-four inches in diameter, the upper being solid and the lower in halves. Between them, and running in grooves, were forty cast-iron balls two-and-a-half inches in diameter, and this appears to be one of the earliest applications of ball bearings to millwork.

In a very few cases, as at Argos Hill Mill, Sussex (Plate XVIII), and Topcroft Mill, Norfolk, a vertical iron track was fixed round the post below the sheers, and iron rollers on brackets bolted to the bottom of the first floor took the place of the steady bearing. No collar was fitted, but at Topcroft Mill a small horizontal track fixed to the quarterbars, was provided for additional vertical rollers. At Bledlow Ridge Mill, an iron-faced wooden track was built up from the six quarterbars and rollers fixed to the bottom of the first floor ran round on it. In all cases the idea was to prevent the mill pitching and rolling about on top of the post. The posts themselves were usually of oak, square at the base where they fitted over the cross-trees and either round or polygonal at the top. Sometimes they were reinforced at the top with an iron plate or samson head as in Saxtead Green Mill, and this was almost standard practice in Suffolk. In Sussex, however—I can recall Argos Hill, Blackboys and Clayton post mills—the post was built up of pieces of pitch pine clamped together; while at Henfield Mill, in the same county, the post was built up of four pieces of oak held together with trenails. Oak was of course the usual timber for the main structure of a post mill; but there were other exceptions. For instance, the post of Moreton Mill, Essex, is said to be of sycamore and most of the timber in Benhall Mill, Suffolk, was of sweet chestnut, while South Elmham St. Michael Mill, Suffolk, had an elm crowntree, deal quarterbars and crosstrees and channel iron sheers.

The roundhouse was not part of the earliest post-mill design, although many later post mills were built *de novo* with roundhouses incorporating the brick piers with the roundhouse wall. They seem often to be an eighteenth-century addition put up to protect the sub-structure and act as a convenient store, and were frequently built when the fan tail was added, as at Framsden Mill in Suffolk. The simplest were of timber, polygonal or round as at Chippenhall Green Mill, Suffolk, now destroyed; but they were as a rule built in brick and a few in stone as at Dale Abbey Mill, Derbyshire (Plate XXVII), of flint in West Suffolk, like that at Drinkstone Mill, and even in clay lump as at Mendlesham Mill in Suffolk. Almost all had two doors opposite each other so that entrance could be obtained safely whatever the position of the sails. Roofs were mostly boarded and latterly covered with tarred felt, but they were also tiled, slated and occasionally thatched, as at Rougham Mill in West Suffolk. Some were very well built, the tiled roof of that at Great Mill, Wickambrook, Suffolk, for example, being plastered inside. All were open at the top, but in some mills the opening was protected by a small petticoat attached to the bottom of the floor of the mill, in others the weatherboarding of the body was carried down over the roundhouse roof and shaped to clear it as at Saxtead Green Mill. Some roundhouses were of small diameter and had no roof, a petticoat on the mill body serving this purpose. This was particularly the case in the Midland type of post mill once most common in Nottinghamshire and extending south as far as Bedfordshire and north into Yorkshire. Normally the roundhouse has no structural significance, but in some of these Midland-type mills a track or curb was fixed to the top of the roundhouse wall, and rollers fixed to the timbers on the bottom of the body, ran round on it to help to steady the mill and to take some of the strain off the post. This can be seen at Cat and Fiddle Mill, Dale Abbey, Derbyshire. At Foston Mill, Lincolnshire, a small bulge on each side at the bottom of the body served as a roof to the small roundhouse, while at Wrawby Mill in the same county the quite considerable roundhouse roof was part of the body; the roundhouse had vertical walls and a tarred canvas petticoat overhung it. At Crowland Mill, also in Lincolnshire, a conical petticoat, suspended from the floor of the body, and over the roundhouse roof, resembled a horse's straw bonnet.

The framing of mill bodies varies considerably in detail, though in the main the ends of the crowntree carry heavy timber side girts running fore and aft, to which the corner posts of the body are attached. Parallel to them, at first-floor level and at the eaves of the roof, are the subsidiary upper and lower side girts, while cross timbers are provided in the form of the breast, tie and tail beams. The tie beams carry the top bearings of any vertical spindles, and the breast and tail beams carry the neck and tail bearings of the windshaft, respectively. In some seventeenth-century mills, however, such as Bourn Mill, and Barley Green Mill, Stradbroke, Suffolk, there are no side girts and instead two vertical members are to be found at each end of the crowntree supporting the upper and lower side girts. The only eighteenth-century post mill to have this feature, at Eye in Suffolk, was built from parts of an earlier mill.

The exterior appearance of the mill bodies varied enormously. Naturally the most marked difference was that between the white-painted and the black weatherboarding, but the proportions varied just as much from the square, squat body at Forncett End Mill, Norfolk, to the high narrow one at Argos Hill Mill, Sussex (Plate XVIII), and a few even had galleries round the eaves as at Tottenhill Mill, Norfolk (Plate IV). Ifield Mill, near Crawley, Sussex, was one of the oddest ever seen; it had a square body with a straight pitched roof coming half-way down as far as the side girts and a tall three-storey roundhouse. Bozeat Mill, in Northamptonshire, was equally curious with a breast that jutted out at the bottom and tapered back towards the top. This was to accommodate the wallower and drive to the stones in front of the brake wheel, instead of behind it as is normally the case. While some bodies were curved others formed an obtuse angle at the centre of the breast and in some cases the breast beam, carrying the neck bearing of the windshaft, was corbelled out, the ends of the upper side girts being extended forwards to carry it. Most bodies were completely boarded with horizontal weather-boards and only Skirlaugh and other Yorkshire post mills come to mind where a body is vertically boarded in the manner so common on the Continent. Some in Sussex were almost completely encased in flat galvanized iron plates, as at Cross-in-Hand Mill (Plate XXVIII), painted white outside, like armoured giants defying the local Don Quixote to do his worst. One of the most curious must have been Thulton Mill, Norfolk, which had its straight pitched roof tiled.

I always think that a porch canopy over the door at the top of the ladder, though unimportant, gives great character to a post mill: lean-to, flat curved, bonnet-shaped and full-width porches, some-times completely enclosed as at Friskney Tofts, Lincolnshire, or open as at Catfield Mill, Norfolk, which is no longer standing but had one of the best examples; and there is a fine drawing of the latter in M. and C. H. B. Quennell's *History of Every Day Things in England*.[1] Paul Sharpe's Mill at Biddenden, Kent, also had an open porch of this type. The mill is said to have been built in 1555 and it was pulled down in 1912. Of it Mr. John Russell of Union Mill,

[1] p. 41 of Vol. II, 1st edition.

The Mills

Cranbrook, Kent, says, 'What few bolts were used in its construction were of the cotter variety. She was quite the smallest mill I have ever been in and was very short. The tail bearing was quite on the back tail frame and the grease used to run down the weatherboards at the back, where there was a small porch, big enough for the miller and a friend to smoke their evening pipes. The stones ran in opposite directions; there were no bins for the stones and the meal bins could not have held more than three bushels. Old Paul Sharpe, from whom the mill took its name, was supposed to have had a personal interview with the devil in Rogley Wood, but I cannot guarantee it.'

The weatherboarding was sometimes plastered inside as at Great Chishill Mill, Cambridgeshire (Plate XXVII), and this kept the mill dry and kept out vermin, but the most apparent internal difference was the arrangement of stones. The earliest post mills had but one pair of stones in the breast, driven direct from the brake wheel. Later came the head and tail stones, with a second or tail wheel, like the brake wheel but as a rule smaller, to drive the rear pair of stones direct. In Kent and Sussex, where a large tail wheel is used, the floor is often lower behind the crowntree to accommodate it; sometimes the tail stones were an addition carried out when the body of the mill was extended to the rear, as at Bourn Mill. This extension beyond the rear corner posts probably had the twofold object of restoring the balance of the body about the post when the heavy shuttered sails were fitted in place of the relatively lighter common cloth spread sails, and to accommodate bolters, already referred to, which came into common use in windmills at about the same time as shuttered sails. Some mills were never properly balanced and remained tilting slightly forward, and these were said to be head sick. This could be corrected by storing bags of grain in the tail of the body; Sprowston Mill, for instance, needed about two tons to keep her on an even keel. The large East Anglian post mills, like Saxtead Green Mill, usually had two pairs of stones in the breast; a few like Friston Mill, Suffolk (Plate XXVIII), had a third pair in the tail underdrift, or driven from below, while Blaxhall, Stanton Chair, and Swilland Mills, all in Suffolk, had four pairs. In a few cases two pairs of underdrift stones were placed on a hurst or framing in the breast, as at Cat and Fiddle Mill and at Brill Mill (Plate XXI), built in 1668, which has been altered from head and tail arrangement in the course of its long life. And while on the subject of alterations, Drinkstone Mill, West Suffolk, dating from 1689 has been turned end for end, the original breast being now the tail and vice versa.

Some post mills, although not large, seemed to be crammed full of auxiliary machinery, bolters, wire machines, jog-scrys or jumpers and oat crushers. As the mills were not, in most cases, designed to accommodate them, their housing and driving presented some awkward problems. Probably the best solution was that found in the Lancashire post mills, all now demolished, which housed them in what can only be described as panniers on either side of the body.

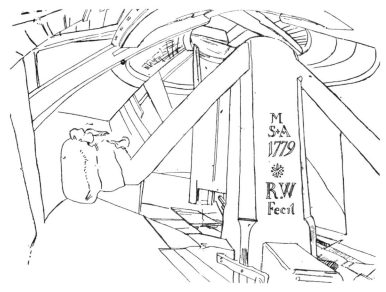

FIG. 14. EYE MILL, SUFFOLK

This is carried to an extreme in the French post mills in the Nord, which have the bolter, the oat crusher and even the office housed in such excrescences. In English post mills without such accommodation the machines were usually housed in the tail of the mill, either across or on either side. Excrescences on the roof were sometimes used to accommodate a larger brake wheel than that originally installed, as at Eye Mill, or an excrescence in the side of the body to permit a larger pair of stones to be used, as at Peasenhall Mill, both in Suffolk.

Carvings on the woodwork of post mills were frequently met with; occasionally they were pictorial and at Chippenhall Green Mill,

Suffolk, which was rebuilt on the site of an older mill, there were on the meal bin two carvings of post mills without roundhouses dated 1712 and 1847 and a smock mill dated 1892. But mostly they were inscriptions with dates and occasionally names with them as at Moreton Mill, Essex, whose post bears the inscription :

Timothy Weedon

Thomas Dagnall

1715

and below it a decorative frieze. But the finest of all was the inscription on Eye Mill, Suffolk, which the late Tom Hennell so beautifully recorded (Fig. 14).

III. CRANBROOK MILL

BAYLEY: But here is a mill sir; will you make a note of it on your plan?
SURVEYOR: In any case—for it is not the least ornament of a manor a well conditioned and a well wrought mill.
JOHN NORDEN: *The Surveyor's Dialogue* (1607).

Of all the variety of smock mills in England none were so widespread and easily recognizable as a family as those of Kent. They have a closer affinity to post mills too, for the cap is like the roof of a post mill both in looks and construction. They vary greatly in detail of course, some black, some white, some with a brick base and some with none, some with a stage round the tower and some without, but the typical mill with its Kentish cap had four patent sails, or sweeps as one must call them south of the Thames, a fantail and an octagonal weatherboarded tower, with a good slope or batter inwards. Of all these smock mills the finest in Kent and the finest in England is still Union Mill, Cranbrook (Title page and Fig. 15). It stands on the edge of the town, which it dominates in the protective way in which a windmill will sometimes dominate a small village. Painted white, with a black tarred octagonal brick base, an iron stage where white and black join, four patent sweeps and a prominent fantail, it has the appearance of lightness due to its excellent proportion which belies its height of seventy-five feet to the ridge of the cap.

Standing in the mill yard, outside the white-painted office, your

FIG. 15. UNION MILL, CRANBROOK

eye travels upwards. First the steps to the door in the tarred brick wall—for Cranbrook is built on a sloping site and has a semi-basement—and above this a loading platform and a loading door. Then

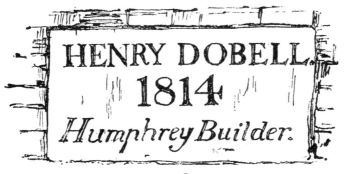

HENRY DOBELL
1814
Humphrey Builder.

FIG. 16.

a white stone let into the brickwork and on it an inscription in black letters (Fig. 16).

James Humphrey was a Cranbrook millwright of some note, and the site of his shop in Waterloo Road is now occupied by Crowden

House, a part of the grammar school. There is a tradition that when the mill was started for the first time Humphrey's son stood on the top of the cap and blew a bugle. On this occasion barley was ground through the french burr stones to soften them down before commencing flour production, beer in quantity was provided and the party amused themselves by pouring some of the barley down the backs of each other's necks. Henry Dobell was addicted to strong drink, and after running the mill for about five years became bankrupt, eventually gravitating to the workhouse, where he died.

A few feet above the inscription is a T iron, one of a series let into the brickwork round the mill, each carrying two iron stays supporting round the third floor the iron stage, which has wooden decking, with spaces between the timbers to let the water through. The white-painted weatherboards covering the timber framework of the upper part of the mill tower start here, and set in them is a two-piece door like a stable door to give access to the stage, with another on the other side. Then you follow the weatherboarding up to a small square window set in the last floor but one, and finally to the cap.

In front of the cap are the four double-shuttered patent sweeps spanning sixty-eight feet, not unlike those on Saxtead post mill. Behind, cocked up at an angle, is the fan stage carrying the six-bladed fan tail (Fig. 17), which through a shaft and bevel gears drives down to an iron worm wheel. This wheel engages with a geared iron rack fixed to the outside of a wooden ring or curb set on top of the tower. The curb is faced with iron plates on top forming a well-greased track, and let into the bottom of the cap frame are brass plates which slide on this. The vertical inside face of the curb is also faced with iron plates and large rollers or truck wheels, fixed to the frame of the cap, run against the curb and keep the cap truly central as it is turned. The spindle on which the worm is mounted is extended through to the outside of the cap, and to the outer end is fixed a small spur-geared pinion. Immediately below this pinion is mounted a large spur gear with a Y wheel fixed to its rim. The wheel is so called because it carries on its periphery a number of wrought-iron forks like Y's. These formerly held an endless rope which passed through two iron stirrup-like guides fixed to the cap and down almost to stage level, and by its means the cap was turned until 1840, when the fantail was put up by George Warren the Hawkhurst millwright. His son William Warren asserted that the millwright who put up the fan on a Peasmarsh windmill geared it up to turn the mill away from the wind and had to add an additional pair of wheels to correct it at his own expense, but this jibe has been told by many millwrights about their rivals. At the same time as the fantail was put up, Medhurst, the Lewes millwright, put in a new wind-

FIG. 17. THE CAP

shaft and replaced the original cloth-spread common sweeps with patent sweeps for which he was the licensee in the south.

In many cases when it was decided to fit patent sweeps in lieu of common sweeps to an existing windshaft, the shaft had to be drilled throughout its whole length to take the striking rod. This was done in place while the mill worked, by using a D-bit which will bore a true hole in metal, and extra lengths about eighteen inches long were shut on or welded to the shank of the bit by the local smith as the work progressed—an example of this being Mr. Norton's smock mill at Meopham Green, Kent. In the case of a wooden shaft, side borings or try holes were taken at intervals to make sure that the boring bit was not wandering due to unevenness of the grain of the timber, and these try holes were subsequently plugged with wood.

The original stage at Cranbrook was made entirely of timber, and was wider than the present one, a wide stage being a convenience to operate the cloths of the common sweeps; it was replaced by the present stage by Warren. Below the fan stage is the striking gear for the patent sails. As at Saxtead Green Mill it consists of a rack and pinion and endless chain, the outer half of which hangs straight down almost to stage level, while the inner half passes over a guide pulley set in an iron stirrup fixed to a wooden guide-pole attached to the fan stage. This arrangement prevents the chain from becoming twisted if the weight at the bottom should swing unduly in a strong wind.

Like many others Cranbrook Mill has had auxiliary power in various forms. At first it was steam power and a ten horse-power steam engine made by Middleton of Southwark was started in 1863. The engine and three pairs of stones were brought from Smarden steam mill, where they had been installed by Sheather the Rye mill-wright, and the driving gear was of Sheather's design and make. The beam engine was replaced in 1890 by a patent rotary steam engine invented and manufactured by Mr. Clarke of the Elwick Ironworks, Ashford. This was unsatisfactory and after working about a year it was thrown out and a Fowler horizontal engine was put in. In 1919, this was superseded by a suction gas plant, which in 1952 gave place to an electric motor.

Up four steps into the mill from the yard and you are on the weighing floor above the basement store. On the two floors above is the modern and purely power-driven machinery which is wholly contained in the brick-built base of the mill tower. On top of this octagonal brick base are heavy wooden sills and at each of the eight corners of the brickwork is a cant post or corner post extending to the top of the tower, where they are tied together by the circular wooden curb, already described. On the third floor, the lowest floor in the timber-built portion of the mill tower, are the bins for the meal produced by the wind-driven stones above. In the ceiling of this floor are the governors and regulating gear controlling the stones, all in iron with the wooden meal spouts coming down at an angle from the stone floor above to the bins. There are the belt-driven governors with their pairs of weights, the steelyards, each with their single weights, and the hand controls for the fine adjustment of the gaps between the stones, the whole covered with a fine white dust which shows up the outlines against the darker woodwork of the mill body. There are two doors opposite each other giving on to the stage which is round this floor, for the first thing that the miller does after start-

FIG. 18. THE STONE FLOOR

ing the mill from the stage is to go to the meal spout and put the stones to work, so the nearer he is to the starting gear the better. At Little Hadham smock mill, Hertfordshire (Plate XXIII), the miller told me that he was once feeling the meal when starting up ready to make the initial adjustment to the stones, when the complete pelt of a mouse fell into his hand with the meal. The mouse had been feeding on the grain in the eye of the stone and being unable to escape passed between the stones and was ground with the corn.

Mr. Elmer once left Woolpit post mill, Suffolk (Plate XXVII), running in a steady breeze while he was attending to the steam mill nearby. When he thought that it was time to refill the hopper of the stones in use he returned to the windmill to find a mouse on the runner stone trotting steadily along the edge of the eye of the stone in the opposite direction to that of the stone's rotation, thus keeping in the same relative position. It had evidently been in the eye of the stone eating grain when the mill was started. Seeing Mr. Elmer, it tried to escape, but only just saved itself from being thrown off the

FIG. 19. A STONE AND TOOLS FOR DRESSING IT

stone by centrifugal force and had to scramble back to the edge of the eye.

'What did you do?' I asked.

'I watched him for several minutes,' said Mr. Elmer, 'then I stopped the mill and let him run away; I thought he deserved it.'

Up another ladder and we reach the stone floor (Fig. 18). There were originally three pairs of stones of which two remain, a pair each of french and peak stones. In Cranbrook Mill the wind-driven french stones are four feet four inches diameter and the peak stones are four feet six inches; both are overdrift as at Saxtead Green Mill, but here it is the great spur wheel that has wooden cogs, while the stone nuts are all iron. A down-turned bevel ring bolted to the arms of the great spur wheel drove two short horizontal shafts, which were put in to drive dressing machines, since removed, and the sack hoist, a very neat arrangement. As at Saxtead Green Mill the stone casings are octagonal and there is a bell alarm; originally the bells hung above the great spur wheel, the arms of which struck the clappers, but now they are sounded by a jockey pulley driven from the belt driving the governors. Each runner stone has an arched wrought-iron bar cemented into it across the eye of the stone (Fig. 19). A recess in this

FIG. 20. THE SACK HOIST

bar rests on the rounded top or cock-head of the stone spindle, which passes up through the bedstone to support the runner. A cast-iron mace, with recesses on either side and at right angles to each other, fits over the stone spindle and its recesses are engaged by the bar and by fork at the lower end of the quant, respectively, thus forming a primitive but effective universal joint.

Ascending again we pass through the bin floor, which holds the grain to be ground by the stones below, to the top at the dust floor below the cap. This is a dark floor open to the cap and unlit except with light from the tail of the cap itself. Here are the sack hoists (Fig. 20), wind and power driven, by which the grain can be

41

hoisted from the ground floor to the bin floor through the double-flap trap doors as at Saxtead Green Mill. Here too, the top of the upright shaft, which carries the great spur wheel in the ceiling of the stone floor, can now be seen carrying the wallower driven by the brake wheel in the cap above. With the aid of the short movable ladder one climbs up through the massive timbers of the cap frame into the cap itself (Fig. 21). Here one is faced with the brake wheel with iron hub and arms, wooden cants, rim and cogs, and a wooden

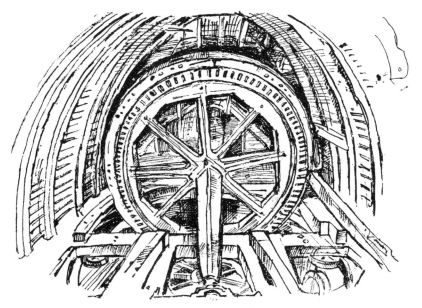

FIG. 21. INSIDE THE CAP

brake to hold it fast. Just below, through the massive timber cap frame on which the whole cap is built up, can be seen the top of the wallower, and the truck wheels centring the cap.

The sounds of the mill at work are different from those in Saxtead Green Mill. You hear the rumble of the brake wheel and wallower in great volume but less of the stones and their drive, and when the fan tail moves you hear the quieter noise of it and its gearing together with the sound of the cap sliding round on the curb. Here, too, can be seen very plainly how the brake operates (Fig. 22). The long timber brake lever, which holds the wooden brake contracted on to the brake wheel, is normally horizontal and the brake is on. The end of the lever is straddled by a wooden trestle, the brake rope fixed to the trestle passes down round a pulley let into the lever itself and then up over two more pulleys let into the top of the trestle, and so down through a hole in the floor of the cap to the stage below. To take the brake off, the rope is pulled and the lever is raised; a pin projecting from the side of the lever engages with a swinging iron catch so designed that it will swing out of the way and then back again and strike the pin. This can be felt right down the brake rope,

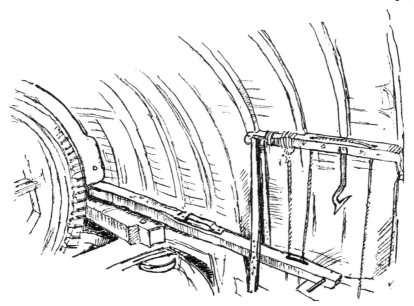

FIG. 22. THE BRAKE

which is immediately loosened and the pin drops into a slot in the catch. The operation is in reverse when putting the brake on, but a sudden application will strain the mill and might even throw a sweep, so it has to be carefully timed. It is also necessary to leave the sweeps standing in the correct manner, normally in the form of a St. Andrew's cross, which equalises the strain on the stocks (or middlings, as they are called south of the Thames), but if the sweeps are to be examined or repaired one pair will be set upright; and if anyone is to get out on to them through the storm hatch in the cap above the neck journal at the front of the windshaft, the front pair of sweeps must be upright.

The Mills

At both Saxtead Green and Union Mill, Cranbrook, each pair of sweeps ('sails' at Saxtead) is bolted and clamped to a middling ('stock' at Saxtead). The two middlings are held in the poll end, cast on the front end of the windshaft. This looks like two open-ended boxes at right angles to each other, and each middling is held fast into one of these by pinch screws at Cranbrook and by wedges at Saxtead Green. The sail frame is built up of transverse sail bars mortised through a backbone called a whip, and connected at their outer ends by hem laths or uplongs. The bars divide the sail frame into bays and in each bay there are three hinged shutters, which at Cranbrook are entirely of wood. To strengthen the middling, wooden clamps are fixed on either side outside the poll end and extending perhaps six feet each side. The whole assembly of two middlings, four complete sweeps and four clamps is extremely heavy and expensive.

In the tail of the cap are the two diagonal timbers which, anchored to the cap frame at their lower ends, project upwards and outwards to support the fan tail and its stage. Climbing out through the rear hatch on the fan stage and standing up, one has a magnificent view and can appreciate the height of the mill and the size of the sails and fantail in a way impossible from the ground or even from the stage below.

In 1932 Mr. Russell's retired miller, Frank Reeves, wrote to Mr. Russell in reminiscent vein and I have permission to quote from him. Apart from a little punctuation I leave the matter as he wrote it:

'Well, the last '32 how different from the present '32; I remember hearing of the Misters J. and G. R. attending to the market business in the smock frocks, very honourable in those days; thirty years later I remember quite a number worn by the ancients. One W. Pullen has been mentioned as one of the early supporters of Union Mills. In my days he and his brother Tom has frequently visited for goods. When waiting between deliveries, "Will you have a little gin, Mr. Pullen?" "Ah! just a *thimble* full," was the usual answer. Gin! Many suited to do a call, either for weekly payments or orders, knowing the gin custom. One old person used to sit holding the glass and chattering, then give a delicate blow on the gin as though she was about to sip a cup of hot tea. There were a number of sips before the glass was quite emptied. A pig pound (if I remember right) existed where

44

FIG. 23. MR. JOHN RUSSELL

your office is, into which a butcher lad jumped out of the way of "The dog" that broke his chain bounding at him. The dog, joyed of his liberty, pursued the butcher no further. The dog I believe used to be fastened to the axle of the mill cart and thus considerably helped on the old loose beachy roads as Golford and all east end was round in my early days. Whether it was *that* dog's skin of which Mr. J. R's cap was made I am not quite sure, but he had such a one.'

When Henry Dobell went bankrupt in 1819 the mill was taken over by his creditors—Samuel Reader, William Buss, William Unicume, Isacc Titford and Andrew Dungey—hence the name Union Mill. Local sketches in verse published in 1819 by Samuel Reader include the following lines:

> For a miller we've Bonnick, and others no doubt,
> Who very good flour serve constantly out,
> And the mill called the UNION, in many good hands,
> Quite ready to satisfy all your demands.

Bonnick had Hockridge water mill and was a rich miller and farmer.

What of the later history of the mill? It was bought by George and John Russell in 1832 from the Union, and run successfully by them, by John alone, by John and his son Ebenezer, by Ebenezer alone, by Hugh, his son, and by Caleb, Hugh's brother, in 1902 and by John, Caleb's son, in 1918. Caleb Russell took off the fantail and took the shutters out of the sweeps in 1912. In 1918 Mr. John Russell (Fig. 23) ran the mill with four cloth-spread common sweeps and no fantail and in 1920 he took four sweeps from Sarre Mill, near Canterbury, and fitted one pair up as spring sweeps. William Warren made a new fan, which Mr. Russell himself fitted in 1921, and in 1922 he put up the remaining two sweeps and fitted them all up as patent sweeps as they are today. Two of the Sarre sweeps are still in use. Mr. Russell made and fitted one new one in 1937 and rebuilt an old one and put it up in 1946. But in 1950 one pitch-pine middling became too tender and the sweeps stopped, for no pitch pine or other suitable timber of large enough dimensions was available in this country at that time. Few millers were ever their own mill-wrights, but Mr. John Russell is miller, millwright and engineer and in his time has done most of the work on the mill himself. He tells me that he put the sweeps and fan tail back for sentiment's sake and that the wind never earned him any profit. Some folk may think him foolish to have done so; most of us will applaud his courage and thank him for the twenty-eight years' additional life he gave to his mill. For, as his man Patterson once said when she was running slowly, 'Wonderful stately, isn't she?'

FIG. 24

IV. THE SMOCK MILL

SPEAKING of his old job, Mr. Bishop, who for twenty-five years was stone-dresser and miller's roundsman at Meopham smock mill, Kent, thus explained the windmill's principles.

'Some people fancy that the weight of those sails hangs all outside the mill. It doesn't, of course; it all balances inside. All that weight rests equally on the neck and tail bearings of the windshaft

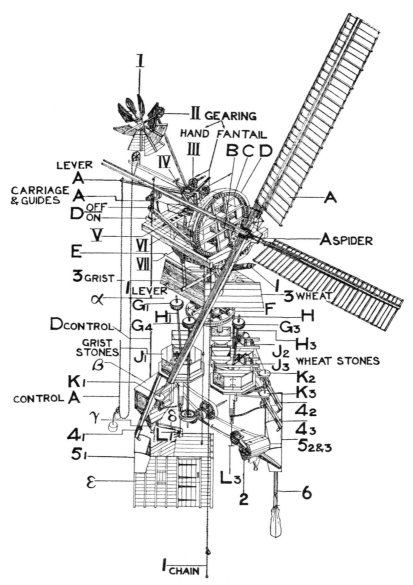

A, Sail and striking gear. B, Windshaft. C, Brake wheel. D, Brake. E, Upright shaft. F, Great spur wheel. G, Stone nuts. H, Quants. J, Stones. K, Governors. L, Adjusting screw.

1, Sack hoist. 2, Smutter. 3, Grain bins. 4, Meal spouts. 5, Meal bins. 6, Spout from meal bin.

SMOCK MILL

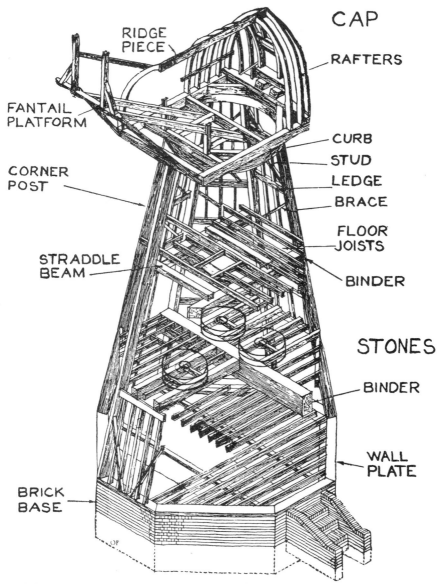

CAP

RIDGE PIECE

RAFTERS

FANTAIL PLATFORM

CURB
STUD
LEDGE
BRACE

CORNER POST

FLOOR JOISTS

STRADDLE BEAM

BINDER

STONES

BINDER

WALL PLATE

BRICK BASE

β, Wire machine. γ, Wire machine flour spout. δ, Wire machine bran spout. ε, Wire machine bran cupboard.

I, Fan. II, Drive from fan. III, Fan reduction gear. IV, Handle for ditto. V, Worm drive to rack. VI, Cap frame. VII, Rack.

FIGS. 25 and 26. SMOCK MILL

that carries the sails. Then the framing of the cap, the sheers and cross-pieces, spreads that weight equally all round the curb of the tower. So then, whichever way the cap is turned, the strain on the tower is always the same. The wallow-wheel and the upright shaft (which take the power down from the brakewheel built on to the windshaft) have to balance just the same, not the least bit out of the upright and level. And then the stones must balance too; the bedstone must be fixed with spirit level, and the runner-stone spin level and even all the time. It was my business as stone-dresser to see that it did; always to dress the stones evenly.' This conception of balance seems to be a very good basis for the understanding of a working windmill.[1]

The smock mill is said to get its name from a fancied resemblance to the obsolete smock frock of the countryman, today to be seen only in museums or used as a fancy dress. The smock mill has a tapering timber-framed tower (Fig. 26), usually on a brick base, and its framing is covered with boards. The height of the base varies from a few feet to several storeys, but it usually extends to first-floor level and it sometimes incorporates a basement. The smock mill at Frieston, Lincolnshire, however, had no brick base, and when burned down in about 1918 it was found to have had a mill-stone as a foundation for each cant or corner post. These posts are laid on sills and taper inwards towards the top where they are joined together by a timber track or curb, on which the cap turns. The cant posts are braced together and tie beams between them support the two main beams carrying each floor, the beams supporting each successive floor being at right angles to those on the floor below. Vertical studding was used in the space between each 'quarter', as the panels between the cant posts were called. This helped to carry the boarding covering the framework, and the varying methods of framing a smock mill are in themselves a study in the art of carpentry. The brick bases are usually octagonal as are the timber-framed towers, but in Kent the octagonal towers were sometimes built on square brick bases, as at Willesborough Mill, near Ashford, sills being placed across the corners of the base.

While the majority of smock mills are eight-sided there are exceptions; thus Shade Mill, Soham, Cambridgeshire, is six-sided, its neighbours at Wicken and Ely are twelve-sided and round, respec-

---

[1] From *The Countryman at Work* by Thomas Hennell.

The Smock Mill

tively, the latter having an octagonal frame inside, while Wangford Mill, Suffolk, which was burned down, was ten-sided. Towers are covered with horizontal weatherboards as a rule, but on either side of the Suffolk-Cambridgeshire border vertical boards were used as at the Wicken and Shade Mills. In such cases the longitudinal butt-joints of the boards were usually covered with smaller boards or laths to make them weathertight. In the case of the horizontal boarding the lap-over of the ends of the boards at the corners was done alternately, first from one side and then from the other, and a lead or zinc strip was sometimes used to cover all these joints from top to bottom. Occasionally an inside lining of plaster was used or an inner layer of boarding, usually horizontal, but sometimes diagonal, as at Eye Green Mill, Peterborough. Some smock mills were tarred, others painted white, the latter being cooler and better looking but much more expensive to keep presentable.

Many smock mills had a stage round the tower, usually at first-floor level. Ideally this was the meal floor below the stone floor, so that the miller could watch the meal, attend to the adjustment of the stones, go out to the stage to regulate the sails and load up the grist cart or wagon.

Two doors opposite each other give on to the stage and this was also the practice on the ground floor too, whether the mill had a stage or not. A few smock mills, such as Cattell's Mill, Willingham, Cambridgeshire (Plate XXV), had a gallery round the cap, but they were not common. Stages were of wood, iron or both and in Kent and occasionally elsewhere they were sometimes supported from the ground by wooden uprights, as at Woodchurch Mill, instead of by brackets from the tower.

The lighting of a smock mill was usually effected by windows and the weather-proofing of frames, owing to the inward slope or batter of the tower, was by no means easy. In fact the great weakness of a smock mill was its vulnerability to the weather; rain drove through the joints at the corners and round the windows and doors, and rotted the sills and the cant posts, which dropped, distorting the curb and preventing the cap from turning.

As in Union Mill, Cranbrook, the drive to the stones in smock mills is always indirect (Fig. 27). The wallower, the first driven wheel in the mill, transmits the power from the brake wheel to the upright shaft, which is centrally located in the mill tower and from which the drive to the stones or other machinery can be taken. The size of the tower varies from large with many floors as at Union Mill, Cranbrook, to small with few floors as at West Wratting Mill, Cambridgeshire. The top floor was usually close to the curb and served to keep dirt from above out of the lower floors and dust from rising out of them into the cap, so it was known as the dust floor. Below it as a rule were one or more bin floors, where grain to be ground was stored in bins. Below this was the stone floor where the grain was ground, and under it the meal floor where the meal from the stones was bagged up and the stones themselves regulated. If this was the first floor the ground floor was used for storing grain before it was hauled up to the bin floor by the sack hoist, which was usually either friction-driven from the underside of the wallower, or driven by slack belt and shafting by a gear on the upright shaft.

Smock mills do not figure in early illustrations of English windmills and it is not possible to say with any accuracy when they were first built over here. At a guess I should expect that it was when Cornelius Vermuyden introduced Dutch-type drainage mills into this country in the reign of James I. The oldest *dated* smock mill I know of is that at West Wratting, on the Cambridgeshire-Suffolk border, which has the date 1726 carved on the brake wheel. It has a round brick base, vertical weatherboarding plastered inside and a pepperpot cap with an acorn finial on top, typical of the mills in the Newmarket area.

However, Mr. Hunt the Soham millwright told me that Ickleton smock mill in Suffolk, pulled down by his firm in the eighties, had a seventeenth-century date stone in the base, which he cut out and gave to the vicar; and incidentally the cap of the mill was thatched. And the smock mill at Lacey Green, Bucks, originally set up at Chesham in the year 1650, was brought to its present position in 1821 when the fantail was added. Small smock mills were occasionally erected on top of other buildings; such a mill is that at West Blatchington near Hove in Sussex on top of a barn, and there was another on top of a workshop at Stopper Lane, Rimington, Lancashire, which had three sizes of wheel on the windshaft to utilise varying wind speeds. In Cambridgeshire, where smock mills were once plentiful and are still to be found, there were two local types; those of the Cambridge area with ogee caps and those of the Soham area with dome-shaped

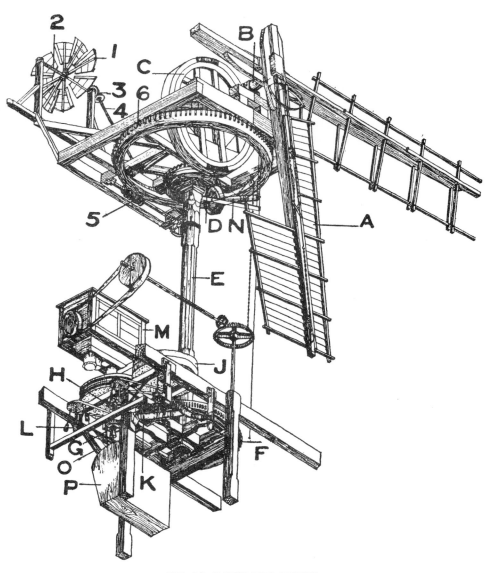

FIG. 27. SMOCK MILL DRIVES

A, Spring sails. B, Windshaft. C, Brake wheel. D, Wallower. E, Upright shaft.
F, Great spur wheel. G, Stone nut (raised out of gear). H, Stone spindle. J, Stones.
K, Bridge tree. L, Governors. M, Wire machine. N, Sack hoist. O, Meal spout.
P, Meal bin.

1, Fan. 2, Fan spindle. 3, Primary drive (bevels). 4, Countershaft. 5, Final
drive worm. 6, Rack.

caps and fantails braced to the top of the cap. The other areas with typical smock mills were South Essex, where the caps were large and boat-shaped, and Kent, where caps were like the roofs of post mills. There were, of course, a number of smock mills elsewhere, as for instance in Sussex, but after the First World War they survived in insufficient numbers to enable one to call them a local type—except the drainage mills, which will be considered later.

V. SIBSEY MILL

NORTH and north-east of the Isle of Ely was a land of brick tower mills with a distinctive ogee or turks-head type of cap with a ball finial, a type to be met with elsewhere, but not so consistently nor with such a strong family likeness. The great number of mills with this type of cap to be found in the corn lands of Lincolnshire, caused it to be known as the Lincolnshire cap; but an early illustration of an ogee cap is in one of John Smeaton's own drawings, of a smock mill at Wakefield, Yorkshire, which he built in 1755. The typical Lincolnshire tower mill had from four to seven floors, was often tarred, with a white-painted cap and four double-shuttered patent sails, while two lattice-braced handrails extended from the cap to the fantail along the upper fantail supports.

It was in Lincolnshire, too, that windmills with more than four sails were most commonly to be found although the earliest illustration of such a mill in England is again a drawing by Smeaton, this time of the five-sailed Chimney Windmill, Newcastle, a smock mill built by him in 1782 and still standing but without its sails. Five-, six- and eight-sailed mills were indeed still at work in Lincolnshire up to 1942, when the last eight-sailed mill at Heckington stopped, and of all the six-sailed mills, Trader Mill, Sibsey, was the finest (Fig. 28). She was also one of the last mills to be built *de novo* in Lincolnshire and was erected on the site of an old post mill in 1877 by Saundersons, a well-known firm of millwrights in Louth, in the traditional Lincolnshire style. They had the distinction of building the last corn windmill in England in 1892 at Much Hadham, Hertfordshire. The Saunderson mills were all well proportioned and Trader Mill is no exception. Particularly pleasant is the wrought-iron

FIG. 28. TRADER MILL, SIBSEY

railing of the stage, twenty-five feet up and one-third of the height of the mill from the ground.

Standing near the mill was a portable steam engine in beautiful order of which the miller, Mr. Ward, was very proud, for Mr. Ward was 'brought up in steam' and had operated steam tractors and ploughing and threshing tackle over a very large area of the country in his time. 'I am a steam man,' Mr. Ward told me many years ago and steam was always his first love.

Mr. Ward was one day working in his mill wearing his overalls

FIG. 29. THE SACK SCALES

when a man entered and asked for Mr. Ward. 'He's not here,' said Mr. Ward.

'Not Mr. Tom Ward?'

'No.'

'Well, where can I find Tommy Ward?'

'That's me,' said Mr. Ward. And it's as Tommy Ward most people thought and talked of him, for he was well known in his part of the country.

Outside the door to the lowest floor there are five steps leading up to a low loading platform—for Trader Mill also has a basement —and inside there is one of the old weighing machines with Gothic Revival decorations (Fig. 29)—once so common and now seldom seen in use. Judging by its style it is as old as the mill and probably took the place of some wooden beam scales, which were commonly

FIG. 30. THE STONE FLOOR

found in old post mills. Trader Mill is only one of many tower mills in Lincolnshire built on the site of older mills—sometimes of smock mills and sometimes of post mills. The six-sailed tower mill at Penny

Hill, Holbeach (Plate XVII), now dismantled, was built on the site of a smock mill of which a drawing has survived (Plate XVa), and the base of the six-sailed tower mill at Billinghay is said to incorporate the roundhouse of a post mill which stood there previously.

The impression inside the mill with its circular whitewashed walls is one of lightness, which seems to increase as one ascends. The first floor is the meal floor and, in accordance with the usual Lincolnshire practice, there is only one pair of governors which regulates all the stones on the floor above—one pair of french from the old post mill and two pairs of peaks or greys as they are often called. The stone floor has two doors opposite each other (Fig. 30), giving out on to the stage, and when open one can see an attractive section of the wrought-iron railing in the foreground and a fine stretch of country-side behind.

The first thing one notices on the stone floor is the slender iron upright shaft carrying a large iron great spur wheel just below the ceiling and terminating in a curious wooden box on the floor at the bottom. By opening catches the box can be removed in two pieces and is seen to be a cover for a belt drive for the governors already seen in the ceiling of the floor below. The stone casings are round and the stones are driven from above with iron stone nuts having wood cogs mortised in. Up through two floors of grain bins and sacks to the dust floor, open to the cap (Fig. 31). Here can be seen the sack-hoist drive (omitted from the drawing for clarity); a flat iron pulley is raised into contact with the underside of the iron wallower mounted on the top of the upright shaft. Arching above are the ribs or rafters of the spacious ogee cap, curving in slightly at the bottom towards the curb and with a reverse curve of equal radius, coming together at the stem of the ball finial in the centre at the top. Looking across at opposite ribs from below in this way one gets something of the effect of a Tudor arch. The cap is double boarded with horizontal boards inside and vertical boards on top. While the Lincolnshire type of cap is distinctive, good to look at and gives a reasonably good air flow behind the sails it does have the disadvantage, being round in plan, of exposing to the weather the ends of the main transverse timber in front, the breast beam or 'rode balk' as it is called in Lincolnshire, carrying the main weight of the wind-shaft and sails, while the front ends of the sheers are also exposed. These sheers are the two parallel main timbers of the cap frame running on either side of the cap. At their rear ends they are also exposed because they support the fan stage; the Kentish type of

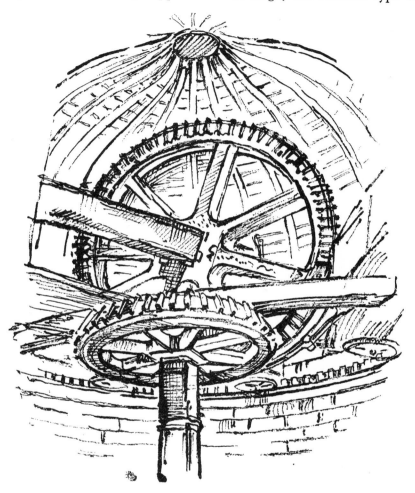

FIG. 31. LOOKING UP INTO THE CAP
The sack hoist is omitted for clarity.

cap does protect all the cap frame members from the weather in a way the Lincolnshire cap cannot.

The curb is of cast iron held down on to the corbelled-out top of the tower by long anchor bolts let into the brickwork. The geared rack for the fantail drive faces inwards and the centring or truck wheels run below a keep flange, which avoids any chance of the cap lifting or ever being blown off should the mill be tailwinded.

Downfield Mill at Soham, Cambridgeshire (Plate XVII), was

FIG. 32. INSIDE THE CAP

tailwinded in 1890. The cap and sails were blown off and the fan rolled at speed across a large field now built over. The mill was a smock mill with an octagonal base and was rebuilt in brick as a tower mill. The result of a fine bit of brick building is unusual and attractive with its octagonal base and round curb, black tarred tower

FIG. 33. TRADER MILL, SIBSEY

and white-painted cap. This mill is also remarkable, like Trader Mill and Union Mill, in having a name; usually in England, if there was more than one mill in a village or town it was identified by the name of the miller. This is not so usual on the Continent of Europe and particularly in the Netherlands where so many mills were built so close to one another that each one was given a fancy name, which might vary from the classical 'Unicorn' to the modern 'Locomotive'.

Climbing from the dust floor up into the spacious cap of Trader Mill, which is sixteen feet in diameter and ten feet high, one sees that all the moving parts are of iron (Fig. 32). The brake wheel is completely of iron, and has iron cogs cast in segments and bolted on to the rim. This made for economy and greater precision in manufacture, for the brake wheel is over eight feet in diameter. The wallower cogs are cast in one piece with the wheel which is only about half the diameter of the brake wheel. The brake is of iron, not wood as at Saxtead Green and Cranbrook Mills, and the curb is built up of cast-iron segments of a circle. When the storm hatch is removed from over the neck bearing of the windshaft, as shown in Fig. 32, one can get outside and examine the sails. In the Lincolnshire type of mill the sail stock or middling is dispensed with and the whip, lengthened and made stouter and called the 'sail back', is fastened by bolts and clamps or bridle irons to a cast-iron cross fixed to the end of the windshaft. This method has a great many advantages but an iron windshaft must be used; there are fewer pieces where water can hang and rot the timber of the sails; there is no sail stock to break and wreck a perfectly sound sail, and the sail back, being little larger in section and no longer than the whip of the other type, is cheaper to replace than the larger and longer stock. Although John Smeaton was the first to illustrate the cross, and possibly invented it, he used only a small one and reinforced his sail backs at the rear with other timbers.

The method of operating the striking gear of the patent sails is different from that employed at Saxtead Green and Cranbrook Mills (Fig. 33). At the rear end of the striking rod which passes through the windshaft, instead of a rack engaging with a pinion there is a block carrying two rollers running in guides, and to the block is fixed a rocking lever extending outside the cap and below the fantail supports. At the end of this lever a chain is hung down to the level of the stage and looped up, over a pulley attached to a timber just below the fan, then down again to the top of the rocking lever. By this means the lever can be pulled up or down and operates the striking rod and shutters in just the same way as the rack and pinion in the other two mills, while weights hung on the chain will have the same effect. There is also a loose wooden distance piece which can be inserted between the sliding block and the tail bearing of the windshaft to hold the rocking lever in the horizontal position

FIG. 34. THE FANTAIL DRIVE TO THE CURB

with the shutters open, and this precaution, together with the brake, are sufficient to prevent the mill starting up on its own. In some of the Cambridgeshire mills built by the Soham millwright firms of Fysons and Hunts, the shutters are held open by holding the rocking lever up with a swinging catch like a brake wheel catch, an example of which can be seen in the tower mill at Swaffham Prior.

Inside the tail of the cap, and to one side of the tail bearing of the windshaft, is the drive from the fantail (Fig. 34). A diagonal shaft, driven through bevel wheels from the fan spindle, terminates in a bevel pinion. This drives the outer of two more bevel pinions mounted together on a horizontal spindle. The inner of the two pinions drives a bevel wheel on a short vertical spindle at the lower end of which is a spur pinion. This in turn drives a spur wheel on a second short vertical spindle at the lower end of which is a second, but larger, spur pinion. This engages the rack on the curb and turns the cap of the mill. To turn the cap by hand the end of the diagonal shaft can be raised up sufficiently to throw the first pair of bevel pinions out of gear and an iron crank or key is applied to the horizontal spindle, but it is a slow operation as the reduction in gear is considerable.

The advantage of a six-sailed mill with a cross to hold the sails is very great when a sail is damaged, for it can be run with four, three or two sails, as was actually the case at Metheringham Mill in Lincolnshire, whereas a five-sailed mill is out of action if one sail is damaged; in 1950 Trader Mill lost a sail, but the opposite sail was removed and the mill has continued to work. It can be said without fear of contradiction that the tall Lincolnshire multi-sailed mills were the finest tower mills ever built in England, and it is not without significance that of the twenty-one mills still at work by wind in England six are in Lincolnshire. But they give the miller plenty of exercise all very well for a man in the prime of life but, as Tommy Ward (Fig. 36) said to me when over seventy, 'Nowadays when A've run up to th' top of th' mill A've to stop and ask meself a question or two.' He died in 1953.

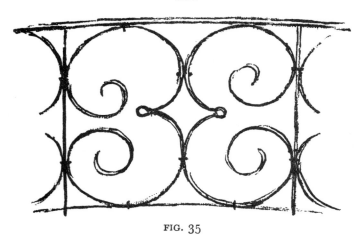

FIG. 35

FIG. 36. TOMMY WARD

VI. THE TOWER MILL

W HEN this type of mill was first seen in England is not known. The earliest illustration of a tower mill is in a French manuscript, *c.* 1420, the the earliest remains of such a mill in England appear to be the so-called beacon at Burton Dassett, Warwickshire. This is actually the two lower floors of a stone-built tower windmill referred to as such in a fifteenth-century deed. Tower mills do not seem to have been common in England for several centuries, however, for the old rhyme

>Glatton round hill,
>Yaxley stone mill,
>And Whittlesey Mere
>Are the three wonders of Huntingdonshire

refers to Black Mill, Yaxley, demolished in 1935. When I visited the mill I saw an inscription M W 1671 on the stonework and the brick piers of a post mill remained in the basement. According to the *Peterborough Advertiser*,[1] however, it is said to have been a Fen lighthouse, to have the dates 1500, 1677 and 1742 and a cellar eighteen feet deep below the mill. Chesterton Mill, Warwickshire (Fig. 37), was built in 1632 as an observatory, it is said, for Sir Edward Peto. It is built of stone and the lower portion consists of six piers, while the machinery is contained in the upper half, in which there are two floors.

The early tower mills were short so that the cloths of their common sails could be set from the ground, while the caps were turned by means of a tail pole with a winch on the end, from which a chain could be run out to one of a number of posts set round the mill and wound up on the winch. Examples still standing and very derelict can be seen at Lutton Gowts and Friskney in Lincolnshire. Although in the Netherlands tall tower and smock mills were built with a stage round the tower from which the sails could be clothed and the tail pole operated, the only English example was the short, squat stone-built tower mill at Deeping St. James, Lincolnshire, and it was not until the advent of the patent sails that tall tower mills began to be built in this country. Many of them were built on the

[1] 4th January, 1927.

sites of post mills and smock mills; Hawridge tower mill, Cholesbury, Bucks, now a house, was built in 1884 on the site of a smock mill, itself only built in 1863. In some cases more than one mill preceded the last mill to be built on the site. An instance of this is Buxhall

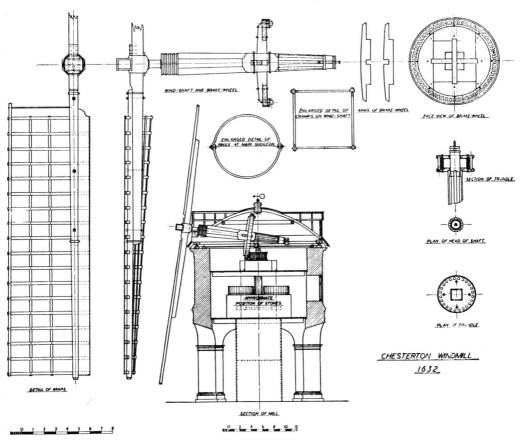

WIND-SHAFT AND BRAKE-WHEEL

ENLARGED DETAIL OF
CRAMPS ON WIND-SHAFT

ARMS OF BRAKE-WHEEL

FACE VIEW OF BRAKE-WHEEL

ENLARGED DETAIL OF
RINGS AT MAIN GUDGEON

SECTION OF TRUNDLE

PLAN OF HEAD OF SHAFT

APPROXIMATE
POSITION OF STONES

PLAN OF TRUNDLE

CHESTERTON WINDMILL
1632

DETAIL OF WHIPS

SECTION OF MILL

FIG. 37. CHESTERTON MILL, WARWICKSHIRE

Mill, Suffolk (Plate III), built in 1860 on the site of a smock mill which replaced a post mill on the same site in 1815.[1]

Like smock mills, the towers of tower mills as a rule have a good batter, since a wide base gives a stability to the tower, most room at the bottom where it is most needed, and a small top which means a small cap and a better airflow behind the sails. Bad design is seen

[1] See Appendix C.

not only in mills where the tower is of nearly equal diameter at base and top as in the case of Old Buckenham Mill, Norfolk (Plate III), or Ashton Mill, Somerset (Plate XXII), but also towers in which the windows are one above the other instead of being spiralled round the tower. Both these faults in design led to cracks in the tower and consequent distortion of the curb which resulted in the jamming of the cap.

Most towers were round but a few such as Lutton Gowts Mill, Lincolnshire, and Littleworth Common Mill, Oxfordshire, are octagonal. An even more attractive mill built in this manner is Gibraltar Mill, Great Bardfield, Essex (Plate XXII); the tower, in a very lovely early eighteenth-century red brick with a steep batter, is octagonal with chamfered corners at the base, sixteen-sided half-way up and round the top. Its history is at present obscure but it has certainly been rebuilt and altered considerably in its time. Kenninghall Mill, Norfolk, is ten-sided, becoming round half-way up, and Downfield Mill, Soham, Cambridgeshire (Plate XVII), has already been described.

The materials of which tower mills are built vary according to the locality; brick is most usual in the east and south and stone in the north and west. Both brick and stone towers were to be found plastered over and frequently the brick towers were tarred and sometimes even painted, in all cases to keep out the wet. Barnack Mill, Peterborough, was naturally of stone but the most curious tower was that of Deeping St. James Mill, which had courses of ashlar alternating with four courses of rough Wittering Pendle walling stone. Yaxley stone mill was of brick and stone plastered and tarred; flint and brick all plastered over form the towers of Burwell (Plate XXV) and Swaffham Prior Mills, Cambridgeshire, and flint rubble plastered over was used for the tower of Wycombe Heath Mill, Holmer Green, Bucks, which collapsed in 1929. At Carleton Rode Mill, Norfolk, the tower is of clay lump cased in brick and Station Mill, Alford, Lincolnshire, has a brick casing round a tower of clunch (a hard chalk). Barrington Mill, Cambridgeshire, still stands with its clunch tower and Big Mill, Burwell, Cambridgeshire, had a clunch tower with walls six feet thick at the base according to Mr. Hunt, who pulled it down. Another clunch-built tower at Waltham, Lincolnshire, collapsed quietly upon itself one wet day while the millwrights from Louth were having their midday dinner in the millhouse. A few brick towers were tile hung—Blackthorne Mill, Oxford-shire, Waddesdon Mill, Bucks, and Halnaker and Polegate Mills, Sussex, are examples, the last named only partly tiled.

Towers ranged from the small three-floor tower at Friskney, Lincolnshire, whose internal economy is said to have come from a watermill at Louth, to the huge Southtown Mill at Yarmouth, Norfolk (Plate III), built in 1812 and demolished in 1905. It was the largest mill ever built in Europe, the brick tower being one hundred and two feet high with a diameter at the ground floor of forty feet and with walls three feet thick, while the total height over the lantern on the top of the cap was one hundred and twenty-two feet. In 1894 it sustained damage in a hurricane which was so severe that it is said to have rolled up lead on the roofs of the churches it struck as if it was paper. The largest tower mill still standing is at Sutton in Norfolk. Built in 1789, it was rebuilt after a fire in 1857 and is nearly eighty feet high. Norfolk, even more than Lincolnshire, was a county for very tall tower mills. Upper Hellesdon Mill, near Norwich, was ninety-five feet to the top of the brickwork and would drive four pairs of stones, a flour machine and an oat crusher all at one time. It had a cast mild-steel windshaft with an eighteen-inch diameter neck journal running on three rollers mounted on gudgeons in the neck bearing; they had cut through the former cast-iron windshaft in six weeks. The mill was struck by lightning two years running and was burnt out in 1914. Green Cap Mill, Yarmouth, was ninety-two feet to the top of the brickwork, and when it was demolished its cap was taken off complete and put first on to Pake-field tower mill, Norfolk, and later on to Beccles tower mill, Suffolk. In Hertfordshire, the eight-sail tower mill at Much Hadham, built by Saundersons of Louth, Lincolnshire, was ninety feet to the top of the brickwork and one hundred and fifteen feet to the top of the ball finial of its ogee cap. The tower was forty feet in diameter at the base and a railway siding ran under the tower so that trucks could be loaded and unloaded direct. Built in 1892 it was dismantled in 1910.

The main areas for tower mills were Norfolk, Lincolnshire, with the Midlands and the north-east, the Lancashire Fylde with Wirral and Anglesey, and Somerset. There were of course a number of tower mills in the south-east also from Cambridgeshire to Sussex, but they did not predominate over timber-built mills to the same extent. The Norfolk type of brick-built mill with the neat Norfolk boat-shaped cap almost covered that county and a small part of north-east Suffolk. The Lincolnshire type with the ogee cap extended, with local variations, from Norfolk to Warwickshire and northwards east of the Pennines to the Tyne. The mills of the north-west had large boat-shaped caps and stone towers large in diameter for their height, while Somerset, an isolated area, had its own tradition of small almost parallel stone towers and wagon-roof caps, sometimes thatched and quite unlike the rest of the country. Although this amounts to extreme simplification, it does give a general idea of the distribution of tower mills.

Towers were frequently heightened and this raising ranged from a few courses, as at Arkley Mill, Hertfordshire, now preserved, to three storeys as in the case of Croft Mill, Lincolnshire, now demolished. The reasons were various and might be from trees growing up or new tall buildings screening the mill from a steady wind, or by the opportunity offered for increased space when patent sails and a fantail were fitted and neither winding the mill nor clothing the sails need be effected any more from the ground.

THE WINDMILL AND ITS SHADOW

'The visibility of motion at a great distance is increased by all that increases the distinct visibility of the moving object. This Saturday, August 3, 1804, in the room immediately under the tower in St. Antonio, as I was musing on the difference, whether ultimate or only of degree, between *auffassen* and *erkennen* (an idea received and an idea acquired) I saw on the top of the distant hills a shadow on the sunny ground moving very fast and wave-like, yet always in the same place, which I should have attributed to the windmill close by, but the windmill (which I saw distinctly too) appeared at rest. On steady gazing, however, (and most plainly with my spyglass) I found that it was not at rest, but that this was its shadow. The windmill itself was white in the sunshine, and there were sunny white clouds at its back, the shadow black on the white ground.'—COLERIDGE, *Anima Poetae*.

FIG. 38. ASHTREE FARM MILL

VII. ASHTREE FARM AND THE DRAINAGE MILLS

EVERYONE who visited the Norfolk Broads before 1939 must
have their own memories of the windmills that at one time
dominated the landscape. My own especial impression is of
the scene from the Acle 'New Road' to Yarmouth from which, in the
mid-twenties, nearly a score of mills could be seen in working order
at all points of the compass—mostly drainage mills, which at the

FIG. 39. SCOOP WHEEL: STUBBS MILL, HICKLING

time were rapidly going out of use before the onslaught of the oil-
engine-driven pump. I have photographic records of over sixty-five of
them, all of which were at work in 1920 as far as I am aware; but
the last one to work by wind was at Ashtree Farm and it had the
sails and part of the windshaft blown off on 1st February, 1953
(Fig. 38). It stands by the south bank of the River Bure, three miles
above Yarmouth, and belongs to the Church Commissioners and not
the Drainage Commissioners, which accounted for its survival.

Typical of the smaller Norfolk drainage mills it was built in 1912
by Smithdales, the millwrights of Acle, on old foundations and stands
about thirty-five feet high, with a well-tarred brick tower, a white-
painted boat-shaped cap with a deep petticoat, a fantail, and had

FIG. 40. ASHTREE FARM MILL

four double-shuttered patent sails spanning forty feet. At the side of
the mill is a semi-circular wooden casing enclosing the fifteen-foot
scoop wheel, which the mill drove. Below the fan stage is a striking
gear for the sails, with a rack and pinion and a Y wheel for the
striking chain, which is kept well clear of the tower and scoop wheel
by a braced tail pole carrying two guide pulleys. As it was not
possible to remove the casing of the scoop wheel a drawing was made
of a wheel of similar construction at Stubbs Mill, Hickling (Fig. 39),
which is double the width (fourteen inches) but almost the same
diameter. The split cast-iron centre with eight arms carries twenty-

FIG. 41. GROUND FLOOR: THE FINAL DRIVE

four wooden floats, connected near their tips by a built-up wrought-
iron ring on each side. The lower half of the wheel fits closely into
a brick-lined culvert, and the upper portion is enclosed with a casing
of weatherboards. The action of the wheel as it turns is to scoop up
the water in the culvert (Fig. 40) and discharge it at a higher level
into the river, the maximum lift being about one-fifth of the diameter
of the wheel. The water is discharged through an opening having a
cast-iron frame and a hinged door, which is closed automatically if
the river level exceeds the discharge level of the wheel.

Unlike a corn mill a drainage mill contains very little machinery;
all that is usually required is two pairs of gears, one in the cap and
one on the ground floor, connected by an upright shaft. Entering the

ground floor, which is only ten feet across, you see the large pit wheel (Fig. 41), so called because it is mounted on the scoop wheel shaft and turns in a pit. It is driven by a bevel wheel on the bottom of the wooden upright shaft, while the hub of the scoop wheel can just be seen through an opening in the brickwork. Since the drawings were made the wooden wheels have been replaced by iron ones from Burgh Mill, near Acle, the pit wheel bearing the inscription W. T. ENGLAND, MILLWRIGHT YARMOUTH 1896. Climbing up through the first floor, empty but for the octagonal wooden upright shaft, we reach the dust floor and look up into the cap (Fig. 42), with its iron

FIG. 42. THE CURB

wallower on top of the upright shaft driven by an iron brake wheel with wood cogs, and round the brake wheel a brake made of wooden blocks fixed to an iron band. The cap is centred by truck wheels running round on an iron curb below a keep flange, but it turns on rollers instead of blocks as at Cranbrook and Sibsey Mills; this is called a live curb and the other system is a dead curb. The drive from the fan is through two pairs of bevel wheels to an iron worm, which engages with a rack on the outside of the curb as at Cranbrook Mill. At the normal speed of 15 r.p.m. of the sails the scoop wheel turned at 105 r.p.m. and lifted eight tons of water per minute, or rather less than half the work that could be done with a modern turbine pump. Some of the drainage mills in the Broads drove a turbine pump of a type invented by Appold which caused a considerable sensation at the 1851 Exhibition. This pump had an efficiency of up to half as much again as the scoop wheel, but none are now left worked by wind. The turbine pump, which is said not to have been the equal of the scoop wheel in gusty weather, in action was not very spectacular; but the scoop wheel, if partly uncovered when at work, could be quite an impressive sight. And if the sea broke through and the scoop wheel had to deal with salt water, masses of foam would be formed until the discharge end of the casing and the outlet channel were covered in it to a depth of several feet.

As in the Norfolk Broads, so in the Suffolk Broads and marshes, the windmills have almost all ceased work. Of the two smock mills belonging to the Somerleyton Estate Trustees, one is typical of the small smock mills that once existed in this area. It is at Herringfleet (Plate XXVI) and is the last orthodox mill at work by wind, while the curious little Priory Mill, St. Olave's (Plate XXVI), close by is also working. Herringfleet Mill, just over one hundred years old, has common sails, cloth spread, and the cap is turned by means of a tail pole. A winch on the end of the pole carries a chain, which can be run out to one of a number of small posts set in the ground round the mill, and then wound up on the winch, thus turning the cap, which runs on wood blocks on a wood curb. The attenuated little four-sided mill at St. Olave's has four patent sails and a fantail and was built in 1910 by Dan England, the Ludham millwright. This mill also drives a scoop wheel, but mills, now derelict, at Minsmere, near Westleton, and Reydon Quay, near Southwold, both in Suffolk, drove pumps through crank shafts, the former with square pistons and cylinders.

The finest drainage mill of all in this area, however, is High Mill, Berney Arms (Fig. 43), on the left bank of the Yare and near Breydon Water. It was built about ninety years ago by Stolworthy, the Yarmouth millwright, for the Berney family and in addition to pumping was used for grinding cement clinker. This was made from mud dredged from the river both here and at Burgh Castle, clinker being sent for grinding from the latter kilns by wherry at a shilling per ton. The grinding was carried out by stones and a pair of these still survive, as do the remains of the kilns, the works office and a few dumps of clinker.

The mill is over seventy feet high, built in red brick, with a stage

FIG. 43. ISOMETRIC DRAWING OF HIGH MILL, BERNEY ARMS, NORFOLK

A, Scoop wheel. B, Stage. C, Gallery. D, Fantail. E. Fan drive. F, Curb. G, Hemlath. H, Whip. J, Bay. K, Shutter. L, Windshaft. M, Poll end. N, Stock. O, Clamps. P, Front striking gear. Q, Striking chain. R, Fan stage. S, Chain guide. T, Cap. U, Sheer. W. Brake wheel. WW. Brake. X. Wallower. Y, Upright shaft. Z, Scoop wheel driving shaft.

round the second floor and a gallery round the cap, which turns on a shot curb. This is a development of the live curb; an independent ring of rollers runs in between two iron tracks, one trough-shaped on top of the curb and one on the bottom of the built-up wooden cap circle, which is bolted to the lower face of the cap frame. The iron upright shaft is in six sections and on the ground floor drives a horizontal shaft through a pair of bevel or mitre wheels, as they are called when of equal size. Instead of the twenty-four foot diameter scoop wheel being close to the mill tower and mounted on the horizontal shaft it is housed in a casing away from the mill and is driven by a spur pinion on the shaft, through an internal gear bolted to the arms of the scoop wheel itself. The mill last worked in 1948 and in 1949 was taken over by the Ancient Monuments Department of the Ministry of Works, who now maintain but do not work it. Incidentally it cannot be reached by road, but only by rail or water.

I have tried unsuccessfully to discover something of the early history of the draining of the Norfolk and Suffolk marshes, but up to the present time no documentary evidence has been forthcoming. It is clear, however, that draining has been done piecemeal. There are portions of marsh detached from the parishes whose names they bear and the mills, which drained from two hundred and fifty to one thousand acres each, sometimes bore names like Chedgrave Detached or Lodden Detached, which was also known as Tom Cook's Mill. In fact the identification of these mills out in the marshes is not easy; where a number stood together they would be known by the names of the marshman who looked after them. For example on the Fleet Dyke in Halvergate Marsh there stood a mill which has been separately identified to me as Halvergate Marsh No. 2, Kerry's Mill and Carter's Mill, and no doubt it has had other names in its day. Another mill took its name from Runham Swim, where cows were swum over night and morning to save a long walk and, in the old days, to save the toll on the 'New Road'; there was hard bottom to the river at this point which was gravelled each year. The mills as we know them seem to have been built from about 1800 to 1914 and in a number of cases to have replaced earlier mills with common sails and a winch to wind them, as at Herringfleet Mill, but with tarred brick towers like those which stood at Tunstall, Toft Monks, Stokesby, and others which survived to our own time.

Of those who built the mills only one firm survives, that of Smith-dale & Sons of Acle. There were a number of others in greater or lesser degree, including Stolworthy, Barnes, Englands of Yarmouth and Englands of Ludham. The Englands claimed to have been the first to put patent sails on a windmill, to have introduced the characteristic Norfolk boat-shaped cap—a most beautiful and efficient design—and to have introduced the patent sail and fantail into Denmark. Dan England of Ludham rebuilt the Horsey drainage mill in 1912, using many of the old parts. The first mill had been built perhaps two hundred years before on the same site and was known as Horsey Black Mill. It was rebuilt in 1897 after the cap had been blown off. In 1912–13 when the present mill was being rebuilt, Dan England decided to take off the cap roof complete as it was in such good order and to re-use it. It was lifted up off the cap circle and was about to be swung aside and lowered when the sails, which were not upright, moved over. The brake had not held, nor had the brake wheel been spragged, and the whole top fell over sideways and was smashed on the ground.

The drainage of the Fens—the lands stretching around behind the Wash—is now well known and documented owing to the researches of Dr. H. C. Darby presented in his fine book *The Drainage of the Fens*, published in 1940, and I quote below a few historical facts relative to windmills culled from it.

The first mention of a drainage windmill in the Fens is to one which stood 'by Satterday Bridge in Holbich' in 1588 and the first illustration of one is contained in *The English Improver Improved* by Walter Blith, published in 1652. R. G. Baker's *Map of the County of Cambridge and the Isle of Ely*, surveyed 1816–20, shows just over two hundred and forty drainage mills, and in 1852 J. A. Clark in *Fen Sketches* estimated that 'the number of windmills formerly at work on the whole of the Fens between Lincoln and Cambridge probably exceeded 700, at present there may be about 50 mills in the Lincolnshire part of the Level and perhaps 170 in the Bedford Level and adjacent Fens or a total of 220'. The disappearance of the windmills was due to steam pumps. The first steam engine was put up along Ten Mile Bank in 1819–20 by the Littleport and Downham District Drainage Board, and in 1838 J. Glynn, in a paper to the Royal Society of Arts entitled 'Drainage of Land by Steam Power', stated: 'In 1830 Littleport Fen, about 28,000 acres, were drained by two steam engines of 30 and 80 horses power with a few of the old wind engines still retained. Before steam power was used there were over seventy five windmills in this district.' The mills disappeared without leaving a trace, for it was all they could do to deal with the floods, but the steam engines drained the water out of the peat as well and the land sank, leaving the windmills high and dry, so that in 1877 S. B. J. Sketchley in *Geology of the Fen Land* could write: 'Hilgay Fen drainage mill wheel originally dipped 6 ft. when the land was bright, that is, just glistened with water, and twenty-six years afterwards it only dipped 20 in. under similar circumstances, showing a compression of 52 in. in that time or an average of 1·7 in. per annum.' But the reader should get Dr. Darby's book to find this and much other material on the subject.

The density of these windmills in the Fens is well shown in water-colour drawings of North Drain, Deeping Fen, Lincolnshire (Plate XV), made between 1828 and 1831, now in the possession of the Spalding Gentlemen's Society. In a stretch of perhaps half a mile sixteen of these windmills can be seen and a large parish might contain fifty. They could be divided roughly into three classes—large as shown in Cotman's drawings, medium as in Deeping Fen drawing, and small. In the 1920's all that remained at work were two large mills at Nordelph and Soham Mere and a handful of small mills, mostly in Adventurers and Wicken Fens, while one was built as late as 1910 in Isleham Fen; all were wooden smock mills and all had common-cloth spread sails. Betty Mill, Nordelph, was demolished in the 1920's; like others of these large mills the tower contained two rooms for the marshman and his family to live in; they were tiny rooms and the smoke from the chimney discharged into the body of the mill and filtered out as best it could. When the wind was gusty huge puffs of smoke would blow back down the chimney and the family would spend their time in the nearby engine house. At East-field Mill, Hickling, in the Norfolk Broads a Mr. and Mrs. Gibbs brought up their twenty-one children in the mill—they did have four floors and it was a brick tower mill, but as a home it must have been rather like the nest of a long-tailed tit. Soham Mere Mill was built by Hunts, the Soham millwrights, in 1867, for two brothers called Horsley at a cost of £1000, and the job did not pay. Mr. T. B. Hunt told me that one brother was tall and stout and of uncertain temper, while the other was short and thin and very good-natured. The tall brother only lived to be seventy-five (said Mr.

Ashtree Farm and the Drainage Mills

Hunt at the age of eighty-nine), but when the short brother was ninety Mr. Clark, who owned the Soham roller mills, met him in the street: 'Well, John, if you live to be one hundred I'll give you half a crown a week.' And the old man lived to be one hundred and seven. Mr. Hunt assured me that he saw the short Mr. Horsley climb up over the tailboard of a moving tumbril when he was over one hundred. In 1948 Soham Mere Mill, having been classed as a 'dangerous structure', was demolished by order of the County Council. It was found impossible to pull it over with a tractor or to blow it up with gunpowder, so in the end eight charges of gelignite had to be used to demolish the dangerous structure!

A drainage mill driving a pair of stones for corn grinding is unusual though not unique; such a mill stood at Weyford Bridge, Stalham, Norfolk, driving a fourteen-foot scoop wheel and a pair of three feet six inches french stones on the first floor. On the other hand from time to time drainage mills no longer required were converted into corn mills. All were smock mills and the first I ever saw was the beautifully proportioned mill at Dyke, Lincolnshire, which was moved from Deeping Fen in 1845, and when re-erected starts from the scoop wheel were used as joists for the second floor. A half full-sized model of the mill was built in 1935 on the site of the old Crackley Mill, Warwickshire, for the late Lord Kenilworth by Messrs. Hunts of Soham under my direction. Salter's Lode Mill, Norfolk (Plate II), is another which seems to have been moved about the same time as Dyke, while North Mill, Wymondham (Plate II), also in Norfolk, was moved from Dilham in 1859; it was sent to Wymondham by rail and the cant posts had to be cut in two to allow them to be transported. After going out of use by wind just before the Second World War it was burnt down in 1949.

At Freckenham on the Suffolk-Cambridgeshire border a converted drainage mill bears the inscription,

THE FIRST GRIST GROUND AT THIS MILL
WAS [BY] MR. INO NORMAN FRECKENHAM JUNE 30TH 1824.

Crowfield Mill, Suffolk, was brought from the marshes by the grandfather of a man who was born in 1859 and Lavender's Mill, Christchurch, Cambridgeshire, was another converted marsh mill. The mill at Holbeach Hurn was erected by the Adventurers of Deeping Fen in 1665 as a drainage mill and was the last in that fen to throw

81

water into the River Welland; it was converted to corn milling in 1803 and was demolished in 1914.[1] There were probably many others also of which I have no record.

So have passed the drainage mills and with them most of those who could build, run and repair them. It was a hard if healthy life living in the Marshes of the Broads. As late as 1947 I myself saw drinking water brought in churns to the marshman's house at Carter's Mill near the Fleet Dyke in a dog cart driven at a good pace across the marsh; for when drained, the marsh is firm and affords wonderful grazing at times when the uplands are dry and bare. Perhaps some day someone will write their history, and it will be a fascinating one in which the windmills will be seen to have played an important part.

VIII. MISCELLANEOUS MILLS

THE composite mill has, with one exception, always been an adaptation—a post mill body taken off its post and placed upon a short tower, on which it turns like the much enlarged cap of a tower mill. While there were others such as Cowick Mill, Yorkshire, and Rishangles, Suffolk, the only four I have actually seen were at Banham (Plate IV) and Thornham in Norfolk, Laver in Essex, and Monk Soham in Suffolk. The design seems to me to adaptation of the Midland type of post mill with a track on top of the roundhouse to carry some of the weight of the mill. Thornham Mill was the most primitive, having a single-storey tower and a tail pole to turn the mill. Banham and Laver Mills had fantails on the top of the roof driving down to a rack on the curb of the tower. Tuxford Mill post mill had twin fantails at the rear and stood beside the Great North Road in the same yard as a small tower mill. The advantage of a composite mill can only be the economical one of using the sound body of a post mill rather than scrapping it, and it is hard to understand why Monk Soham Mill was built outright as a composite mill. It had a fantail and a single driven wheel placed centrally in the fan carriage at the bottom of the ladder, which two small outrigger wheels supported.

[1] *The Lincolnshire, Boston & Spalding Free Press*, 14th April, 1914.

Miscellaneous Mills

Hollow post mills were a Dutch invention in 1430, when they were first used for drainage purposes. They consist in essence of a much reduced post mill body in which the brake wheel drives a wallower, which is mounted on top of an upright shaft passing down through the centre of the post to drive machinery below. Only a few seem to have been built in England; the earliest known to me was the mill Parson Hale had built in 1750 on top of Newgate Prison, London, driving bellows to ventilate the prison and thus to mitigate the terrible effects of gaol fever. Although not a great mechanical success it became a visible symbol, which helped to stir the public conscience in the matter of prison reform. Another was erected to grind flint and bones in Southwark, London, adjacent to Barclay's Brewery and the site of the old Globe Theatre. Both mills have long since disappeared.

On Wimbledon Common, Surrey, a grant of a quarter of an acre of land was made in 1816 to Charles March, carpenter of Roehampton, to build a mill for the benefit of the inhabitants of the Manors of Putney and Wimbledon. A hollow post mill was built in the following year and in 1818 a further half-acre was granted for the erection of the miller's cottage. The mill, which was turned by a fantail, was rebuilt in 1893 as a composite mill by Mr. John Saunderson of Louth, and the mill cottage is now celebrated for the fact that in it Lord Baden-Powell wrote *Scouting for Boys* in 1908.

At West Ashling in Sussex there is an all-metal example of a hollow post mill, built in 1861 and perched up like a robot on the top of a water mill. It drove three pairs of stones which bear the date 1859, and from the style of its design this might well be the date of the extension of the water mill building itself, erected originally as a paper mill. In Norfolk at Irstead near Acle on the River Bure, and Starston on a tributary of the River Waveney, were two similar skeleton hollow post mills each winded by a large weather vane and driving a reciprocating pump through a crank on the windshaft (Plate V); there were others which I never saw. At Southwold in Suffolk, there was once a very primitive skeleton hollow post mill used for pumping sea water for the salt pans, which had a strong family likeness to those used in New England, U.S.A., for the same purpose.

Bennett and Elton quote the Oleron Laws adopted in England about the year 1314: 'Some mills are altogether held above the ground and have a high ladder; some have their foot fixed in the ground being as people say, well affixed.' This would appear to be the earliest reference at present known to sunk post mills.

No example of the sunk post mill survives in England. In this type of post mill the substructure was sunk into the ground leaving the bottom of the body a few feet above the ground. The object was evidently to provide stability and minimise the risk of the mill being blown over. The disadvantages were that the height of the mill and the length of the sails were reduced and the substructure was liable to deterioration which could not be seen. A sketch of such a mill at Birkdale, near Southport, Lancashire, is reproduced in Volume II of Bennett and Elton's *History of Corn Milling*, together with a reference to the remains of another unearthed at Aughton, near Liverpool. Similar remains were excavated in the round barrow at Weyhill, Hampshire, in 1911, at Hayling Island, Hampshire, and also in some unspecified barrows in Yorkshire by J. R. Mortimer.

In 1933 Sandon Mount, Hertfordshire, was excavated and remains were found of the horizontal crosstrees of a sunk post mill. They corresponded in all visible detail to the crosstrees of a small normal post mill; the diagonal quarterbars had rotted away, but the places where they joined the crosstrees were clearly visible, the vertical post had gradually rotted down and this accounted for the rotting of the crosstrees at the centre. The Mount was found to be an earthwork thrown up in the thirteenth century and used by the windmill builders a century or so later.

Windmills in Seistan, Persia, are referred to by al-Mas'udi, an Arabian geographer of Bagdad, in 915 A.D. in his book *Meadows of Gold*. Windmills still exist there and are of the type known as the horizontal windmill, in which the sails are mounted on a vertical windshaft and revolve in a horizontal plane. Horizontal windmills of various kinds have been proposed, invented and re-invented in this country for over two hundred years, but the only type to be seen in use here today is the S rotor, the invention of Savonius, a Finnish engineer, which can be seen revolving on the tops of ventilated motor vans.

However, at least three serious attempts were made by Captain Stephen Hooper to make a success of the horizontal mill. His first was erected on his property at Margate, Kent (Plate VI), at the end of the eighteenth century and consisted of a two-storey building on top of which was a large wheel about twenty-eight feet in diameter and forty-eight feet high, fitted with vanes like a paddle wheel and revolving in a horizontal plane. This was surrounded by a concentric casing formed of slats, very similar to the guide vanes of a turbine and which, by turning on their axes like a venetian blind, could be opened or closed at will so as to allow the wind to act on one half of the wheel, the other half being screened. The shaft on which the wheel was keyed was carried down into the tower and drove five pairs of stones in the usual way. The mill stood for a good many years and was working in 1825, but soon after it was so damaged in a severe gale that it ultimately had to be taken down. Captain Hooper meanwhile had sold his property in Margate soon after 1801 and removed to London, settling at Walworth.

The horizontal mill at Battersea, then in Surrey, was built to Hooper's design (Plate VII) in 1788 on part of the site of Boling-broke House for one Hodgson, a maltster, and was designed for grinding linseed. Its dimensions, quoted by Edward Walford in *London Old and New*, do not seem to be correct in all respects. The total height is given as one hundred and forty feet and the diameter of the wheel casing as tapering from fifty-four feet to forty-five feet at the top, and made up of ninety-six movable shutters, eighty feet long and nine inches wide. But if the number and size of the shutters is correct the diameter of the casing was twenty-seven feet taking into account the width of the uprights forming the framing. The main shaft is given as carrying ninety-six double vanes, eighty feet long, and as driving six pairs of stones. The expense of upkeep was very heavy and after falling into disrepair it was taken down in 1849 when Battersea Park was laid out.

In *An Account of the Commencement and Progress of Sinking Wells, at Sheerness, Harwich and Languard Fort. 1797* we read: 'All the works of the Ordnance at Sheerness, and Landguard Fort, including the well-sinking, were under the direction of Captain Page, Mr. Cole, Mr. Hooper of Margate (who made the horizontal windmill at the Sheerness well), and also the well-sinkers, were under Captain Page's superintendence and orders, as the commanding engineer. ... The machinery of the well is made to draw water by wind or horses, in calm weather by the latter, but never to have the two powers of wind and horses used at the same time. This operation should be under the care of a skilful man, to reside on the spot.'

The Mills

The idea of a wind and water mill combined must always have been attractive both to the windmiller, who suffered long calms, and to the watermiller, who suffered from long droughts, and in a few cases it was achieved. There was formerly one at Wandsworth, Surrey, used for rasping logwood for dye, and a corn mill at Helsby, Cheshire, its ruined tower being pictured by Bennett and Elton; another with the windmill tower burnt out stands at Burnham Market, Norfolk, while West Ashling hollow post mill, in Sussex, has already been mentioned. Bishopstone tide mill, in Sussex, had a small smock mill on the roof used only for operating the sack hoist when the tide could not be used. At Little Cressingham tower mill, Norfolk, one water wheel operated the sack hoist and two pairs of stones, the windmill worked a second sack hoist and two more pairs of stones, and a second water wheel pumped water up to the Hall. Wardington Mill, Oxfordshire, is a dismantled tower mill joined to a ruined water mill; South Ockendon smock mill, Essex, built at the edge of a mill pond, once had a water wheel driving a single pair of stones in the basement, and Doolittle Mill, Tottenhoe, Bedfordshire, had an overshot wheel driving the gear on the two lower floors while the tower mill above drove two pairs of stones on the second floor; in 1939 it had been in the Buckmaster family for at least two hundred years. Hibaldstow tower mill, Lincolnshire, has lost cap, sails and water wheel but what remains includes eight radial vaulted chambers on the first floor, some of which were at one time lived in, one having a fireplace; in this respect it is reminiscent of the 'cavier' windmills of the Loire Valley.

Legbourne tower mill, Lincolnshire, was built in 1847, beside a water mill, which had existed as a monastic mill that has been worked by the Davy family for over six hundred years first as tenants of Louth Abbey and later as owners. Both this windmill and the present water wheel were built by Saundersons of Louth and both drove the same pairs of stones on the first floor underdrift by water and overdrift by wind, with two complete sets of gearing. There was a small water wheel which came into action when the water went over the top of the sluice, and a string on this wheel rang a bell in the miller's bedroom. When the bricklayer who built this windmill tower got as far as the top window he 'went on the booze' and continued the tower upwards out of plumb. For this reason eventually four teeth of the pinion of the fan drive, engaging with the rack on the curb, broke and mounted the rack, and the strain split the brickwork of the tower.

Melin y Bont, Bryn dû, Anglesey (Plate IV), spanned the mill stream fed from a pool in front of the mill, and owing to the slope of the ground there were two ground floors. The iron upright shaft ran right through the mill from bottom to top and could be driven by wind from above or by an undershot water wheel on the lower ground floor Two dog clutches on the upright shaft were provided; one on the upper ground floor could be lifted out of engagement by a portable lever and pivot known as a monkey, and disengaged the drive from the water wheel. Two floors higher was a clutch for the wind drive raised out of gear by a jack in a fixed iron frame.

1a. Drainage mill, Algarkirk Fen, Lincolnshire, by W. Brand, 1796.

1b. The Good Intent corn mill, Boston, Lincolnshire, by W. Brand, 1796.

11a. Cooke's Mill, Stalham, Norfolk, built 1797, the first to have Cubitt's patent sails. Burnt down 1903.

11b. North Mill, Wymondham, Norfolk, moved from Dilham 1856. Burnt down 1949.

11c. Salter's Lode Mill, Norfolk, converted from draining to grinding, now derelict.

111c. Old Buckenham Mill, Norfolk, built 1818, now derelict.

111b. Southtown Mill, Yarmouth, Norfolk, built 1812, demolished 1905.

111a. Buxhall Mill, Suffolk, with Catchpole's 'sky scrapers', built 1860, now derelict.

IV*a*. Tottenhill Mill, Norfolk.

IV*b*. Banham composite mill, Norfolk, moved from Hingham.

IV*c*. Melin y Bont, Bryn-dû, Angelsey, now derelict.

v. Hollow post mill used for drainage, Norfolk, c. 1860.

VI. Hooper's horizontal mill, Margate.

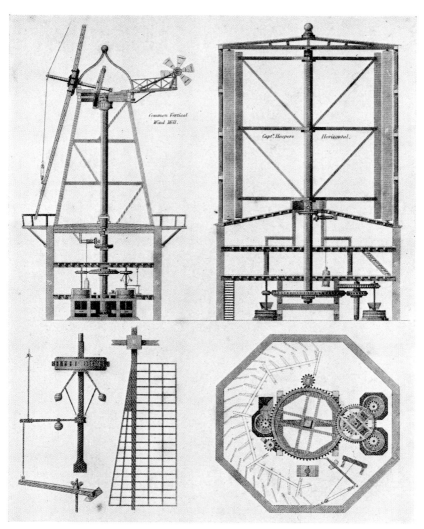

VII. Chimney Mill, Newcastle, and Fowler's horizontal mill, Battersea, Surrey.

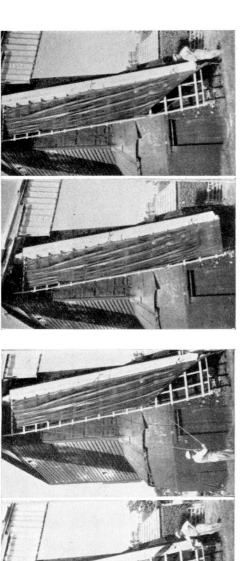

VIIIa–d. Setting common sails at Keysoe Mill, Bedfordshire. e–g. Adjusting spring sails at Wrawby Mill, Lincolnshire.

PART TWO

The Machinery

PART TWO

The Machinery

★

IX. THE SAILS

By God's fair air,
I grind ye grain,
Make good prayer,
When bread ye gain.
(Verse once to be seen in several mills.)

THE essential parts of a windmill sail are the sail proper (Fig. 43), which is built up on a backbone of timber called the whip, and comprises transverse sail bars, and longitudinal laths or uplongs. The whip is clamped and bolted to the stock, a longer and stouter piece of timber, which passes through and is wedged into the end of the windshaft, or through a cast-iron box or poll end (Plate XVII), and carries two sails, two other sails being carried on another stock at right angles to the first one. To strengthen the stocks wooden clamps are often used, sometimes before or behind one to a sail as in Anglesey, but more often on either side of the poll end and extending some way beyond it. In Lincolnshire and the north stocks are dispensed with, and the whip, lengthened and made stouter and called the sail back, is fastened by bolts and clamps or bridle irons to an iron cross fixed to the end of the windshaft. This appears to be the invention of John Smeaton; the first record of such a cross is in a drawing of his dated 1754, of a smock mill at Wakefield (Plate IX) designed by him, and we have it on his own authority that he was the first to introduce the use of cast iron into millwork. Until the time of the First World War, memel fir was used for stocks and

91

The Machinery

backs in England if possible, but pitch pine was later used on account of cost. Stocks could be from twenty-five to forty feet long and sails have a span of from fifty-five to eighty feet. The advantage of the Lincolnshire cross fixing is that a badly damaged sail involves only one sail back, while with the poll-type fixing it usually means a damaged whip and a stock into the bargain. In addition, water remains in the poll and rots the stock which in consequence often snaps at the centre, while water will not so easily lie between a back and the cross to which it is clamped.

The first sails as shown in early illustrations were frameworks of wood, forming flat planes having a constant angle to the windshaft of about twenty degrees throughout their entire length (see tail piece of appendix B.). The sail cloths were laced in and out of the bars and made fast top and bottom; they were furled by being drawn towards the whips at the centre like curtains. The common sail came next with a lattice-like framework and varying angles of weather (Plate I), which may be compared to the pitch of a propeller. This improvement was discovered empirically by the old millwrights, and therefore varies in different districts, the angles varying throughout their length from less than zero to twenty-two and a half degrees. John Smeaton in his *Experimental Enquiry* concerning windmill sails published a number of experiments which he had undertaken with a view to finding the best design of sail. His main deductions were:

(1) That the tip velocity of windmill sails is nearly in direct proportion to the velocity of the wind.

(2) That the load at the maximum is nearly proportional to the square of the velocity of the wind.

(3) That the effect, that is power developed, for the sails at the maximum is nearly proportional to the cube of the velocity of the wind.

The sail cloth is held at the inner end of the sail frame by rings on an iron rail running the full width of the sail. The rings are corded to eyelets in the cloth and cords run down the whole length of the selvedge on either side, enabling the cloth to be spread over the frame of the sail and fastened at the bottom (Plate VIII). By means of other cords called pointing lines, the cloth can be rolled up so as to cut off the outer corner in a greater or lesser degree according to the strength of the wind and the power required. These pointing lines give four settings of the sails known as first reef, sword point, dagger point and full sail. When not in use the cloth is unfastened at the bottom of the sail, twisted up into a long roll and hooked over one or more wooden cleats on the front of the whip, which also serve to hold a loop of cord on the selvedge when the cloths are spread.

Each cloth had to be set or furled by hand, one at a time, and for this purpose each sail had to be brought round to the lowest position in turn. It often necessitated braking the mill in full sail and sometimes stones had to be choked with grain to help the slowing down process for fear of firing the brake. At best it was an unpleasant operation, and often a dangerous job, in wet or stormy weather, and in frosty weather, wet sail cloths would freeze as hard as boards. Many an accident is said to have occurred to millers who have been on the sails when they have started to turn through being improperly braked. In 1772 Andrew Meikle, the Scottish millwright, who invented the threshing machine, produced the spring sail (Plate VIII). In this type of sail a number of hinged shutters of wood or of canvas, on frames of iron rod or of wood, take the place of the sail cloth. They are all connected, like the shutters of a venetian blind, by means of iron cranks to a wooden shutter bar running parallel to the whip. A longitudinal movement of this bar therefore opens and closes all the shutters simultaneously and this movement is controlled either by a coil spring running up the front of the whip, or by a quarter-elliptic, half-elliptic or double-half-elliptic leaf spring, usually at the inner end of the sail, in which the tension can be varied by a slotted or perforated metal strap, a screw, gearing, or some similar device. According to the tension of the spring a greater or lesser wind-pressure is required to open the shutters and spill the wind while the mill is at work. Meikle's original sketch, sent to John Smeaton and preserved among Smeaton's drawings in the library of the Royal Society, shows each shutter controlled by an independent coil spring. It would be interesting to know if, as seems probable, the connecting together of all the shutters was Smeaton's suggestion, but there is no record of his reply to Meikle. This type of sail does not give the power of a good common sail, and it was quite usual to run with two common and two spring sails on the mill, thus ensuring a fair driving power with a certain amount of self-regulation (Plate XXI). The miller at Foston in Lincolnshire went further in 1913 and made himself two sails of which the inner halves were spring sails and the outer halves common sails, the whips being made from old telegraph poles that once stood by the mill along the Great North Road which was being re-poled at the time.

Spring sails, like common sails, suffer under the disadvantage that each one must be set by hand individually with the mill at rest; further, when at work, as each spring sail comes to the lowest position it is screened by the body of the mill, the shutters close with a snap and in wet weather throw a shower of drops against the breast of the mill, necessitating a considerable degree of weather-proofing.

In 1789[1] Captain Stephen Hooper patented what came to be known as the roller reefing sail (Plate XIII) in which a number of small roller blinds were substituted for the shutters of the ordinary spring sail, the bottom of each blind being attached to the top of the blind below it by two webbing straps called listings. The two shutter bars on the sail were operated by two wooden rods known as air poles, the remainder of the striking gear being similar to that of the ordinary patent sail. The object of all this was to alter the effective sail area according to the power required by rolling up or unrolling the blinds, and while this was effected without stopping the mill it was not automatic, although Hooper claimed that it was, and the sails gave a good deal of trouble owing to the breaking of the listings. A number of mills in Yorkshire were to be found with this type of sail, including several post mills, and tower mills at Tollerton, near York, and Seaton Ross in the East Riding. The last was a five-sailed mill and was built on the site of an earlier post mill, the post and crown-tree of the old mill being used as a support for the first floor, while the old windshaft was used as the tail beam to carry the thrust bearing of the windshaft of the new mill; it was demolished in 1953. In North Lincolnshire post mills were also fitted with roller reefing sails; some had only two, either spring, common or patent sails making up the four, but all have now disappeared.

In an advertisement in *The Kentish Gazette* of 11th to 15th March, 1791, Hooper stated:

'These vanes may be had by applying to the Patentee at Margate; and for proof of the facts stated in this advertisement, and the utility of the invention, the Public are requested to inquire of Mr. Fenn and Mr. James Russell, millers at Deal, each person having a mill fixed with the patent vanes, and have worked the same nearly all the

[1] Specification, No. 1706.

present winter; and another now affixing on the mill belonging to Mr. John White, of upper Deal.

'As many persons may prefer having the vanes made by their own Millwright; in that case the Patentee will grant liberty for the same, on receiving a premium of TEN GUINEAS for vanes not exceeding thirty feet in length, and four feet six in width; and in proportion for those on an expanded or contracted scale.'

When patent sails were used they were, of course, coupled to the roller reefing sails and made them automatic. In 1804, Bywaters, of Nottingham, took out a patent[1] for a roller reefing gear, the rollers being parallel to the sail back and clothing the whole length of the sail at once. These sails were at one time in use at the four-sailed mill at Sibsey in Lincolnshire, but none now remain.

In 1807, Mr. (afterwards Sir) William Cubitt (Plate X) introduced his 'Patent sail',[2] which is the most common type to be found in England today, but it is almost unknown abroad, save in Denmark, where it was introduced by English millwrights, and also in Germany and the north of the Netherlands. A pen and wash drawing by William Cubitt in my possession (Plate XI) shows the principle fairly clearly; it combines the shutters of the spring sail with the remote control of the roller reefing sail and is automatic. All the shutter bars or sail rods controlling the vanes are connected by bell cranks to a spider coupling like a cross, projecting in front of the windshaft. The windshaft is hollow throughout its length, and an iron rod called the striking rod passes through it, being fixed to the spider in front and to the rack at the rear.

Gearing into the rack is a pinion mounted on an iron spindle carrying a chain wheel. Over this chain wheel hangs an endless chain to which is hung a weight. To open the shutters the wind must exert a pressure greater than the effect of the weight—in other words it must raise it. It will be readily seen that by manipulating the endless chain, the mill can be regulated while running, and sailed in or sailed out at will without touching the sails, very much in the manner of opening and closing an umbrella. A variation of this is to attach the end of the striking rod by various means to a rocking lever, the ends of the chain being attached to it and the chain hanging down to the ground and being looped up over a pulley in a bar fixed to the fan frame and down to the lever. A block and small wheeled

[1] Specification, No. 2782.   [2] Specification, No. 3041.

carriage are sometimes used to connect the striking rod and rocking lever, and occasionally a double rack and two geared quadrants. This seems to be an adaptation of an invention by Robert Sutton of Barton-on-Humber, Lincolnshire, in 1800. The first mill to be fitted with Cubitt's patent sails was Mr. Cooke's smock mill at Stalham, Norfolk (Plate II), when Cubitt was still working in his father's mill at Bacton; he had been bound apprentice to a cabinet maker at Stalham and married a niece of Mrs. Cooke's. The mill was erected by Samuel Cooke in 1797, and on March the 20th of that year he insured the property for £800 and the contents for £200. The sails were twenty-nine feet long and the windshaft weighed seven tons; a friction-driven governor on the windshaft operated the striking gear. In 1812, during the machine breaking and incendiary fires period, it was Mr. Cooke's custom to go to the top of the mill last thing at night, and on one occasion he counted thirteen fires. In 1848 a steam engine was installed and the stones could be driven by wind and steam at the same time by means of a coarse pitch ratchet and two pawls inserted in the drive, which prevented the engine driving the mill. The mill was totally destroyed by fire on the morning of 6th January, 1903.[1] Cubitt evidently had windmills in his head all through his life. When he was dying those in charge of him were obliged to get toy windmills, which were pulled with a string to make the sails go round, in order to amuse him. Another claimant for the first mill to be fitted with Cubitt's patent sails was Horning post mill; it is said that the sails were twenty-eight feet long and nine feet wide with iron shutters, and Englands, the Ludham millwrights, claimed that their firm carried out the work. It is possible that it was the first post mill to be fitted with patent sails, which were subsequently made under licence by millwrights all over the country.

The frame of a sail is usually braced at definite intervals with back-stays from the whip to the hemlath or outside rule at the trailing edge of the sail; these intervals in the case of shuttered sails are as a rule every three shutters, starting from the inner end of the sail, and are known as bays; and the last bay often contains only two shutters. The number of shutters per bay varies, however, and in Lancashire one shutter per bay could be found. Sails could be double or single, that is with working surfaces on one or both sides of the whip or back, one side being termed the leading side and the other the

[1] *The Miller*, 2nd February, 1903.

driving side. They could also revolve clockwise or anti-clockwise, and the latter (seen facing the sails) was the most common. The earliest sails were double and had the working surface equally divided; the common sail was usually single, and had a leading board on the leading edge of the sail, a primitive form of stream-lining.

The shutters themselves were either of wood, or framed in wood or stout iron wire and covered in canvas, and in all cases they were painted white. At either end of the inner edge of each shutter was a casting carrying a pivot on which the shutter hinged, and at one end the pivot was incorporated in a crank casting which was attached to the shutter bar and enabled the opening and closing of the shutters to be effected (Fig. 44).

Shuttered sails were to be found both double and single, but in some cases conversions have been made from double to single and I witnessed and photographed such an alteration being effected at Waltham Mill, near Grimsby in Lincolnshire (Plate XXIV), in 1928. It has been found that the single-shuttered sail with a light leading board at the best angle of twenty-two and a half degrees will work in lighter winds than the double-shuttered sail, which will act as a brake when sailed out in a light wind. In Sussex the practice was to have double-shuttered sails with a narrow leading side, only the outer half of which carried shutters, the inner half was a very wide leading board or dead lead as it was called (Plate XVIII). Shuttered sails varied in width from six feet upwards, those at Sutton near Stalham being ten feet wide, and shutters varied in width from seven to twelve inches and in length from one to six feet. The large smock mill at Stalham previously mentioned had two double-shuttered sails and two sails with four rows of shutters and a total width of thirteen feet ten inches.

In Lancashire and the north-west, sails tapered and might be eleven feet wide at the inner end and only eight feet six inches wide at the tip, and in the case of patent sails all the shutters were of different lengths. Sails were sometimes braced one to another as at Heckington in Lincolnshire (Plate XIII), where they were braced at the tip with three-quarter inch diameter iron rods, and at Clifton in Lancashire (Plate XXI), where they were braced two-thirds way down the sail. That these braces were subjected to strain is shown by the fact that at Clifton when taut at the top position there was three-quarter inch slack at the bottom position. Sails have to be carefully balanced to run easily, for although the actual revolutions per minute may not be very great—12 to 16 r.p.m. in England seem to be usual speeds—the velocity at the tip is very high and uneven balancing throws a considerable strain on the sails and bearings of the shaft besides making it difficult to get any sail to the lowest position when required. Shuttered sails are by no means faultless and the shutters can freeze up in a frost so hard that it is impossible to move them.

Spring patent sails, as their name suggests, combine the features of both spring and patent sails. Three of several examples still to be seen are on the tower mills at Patcham near Brighton in Sussex, Stoke Ferry in Norfolk, and on the smock mill at Outwood in Surrey. In the first two examples the spider on the end of the striking rod is built up of leaf springs instead of being a solid forging or casting, and in the last a double half-elliptic spring is interposed between the bell crank and the shutter bar of each sail. The old four-sailed post mill at Kingston, near Lewes in Sussex, also had spring patent sails of this description. They were the invention of Cheal of Lewes, who had a very nice model of this spring patent gear in his shop window. Clifton Mill in Lancashire has double-shuttered patent sails with spring-controlled shutters on the driving side only.

In the derelict post mill at Windmill Hill, near Hurstmonceux, in Sussex, an attempt was made to apply a centrifugal governor to the striking gear of the patent sails in addition to the ordinary chain and weight arrangement. This mill had a double roundhouse, one inside and sprouting out above the other, and was raised to clear some trees planted near it by an unfriendly neighbour to prevent the mill getting a good wind. As the trees are planted in the north-east quarter, however, they can have made very little difference to the working of the mill. The tower mill at Clayton, near Brighton, is said to have had a similar arrangement for governing the sails, as did the annular-sailed mill at Haverhill referred to below. The first suggestion of applying the governor to sails is contained in Thomas Mead's patent of 1787, No. 1628.

An attempt to produce an effective air brake was to be found in Catchpole's sky-scrapers. The device consisted of two long shutters placed side by side running parallel to the whip at the outer end of the leading edge of each sail, and controlled by the same mechanism as the ordinary shutters. When closed they gave additional sail area, when open they presented a surface opposed to the direction of motion, and in both cases at the tip of the sail where the effect is greatest; Buxhall (Plate III), Drinkstone and Gedding Mills, all in Suffolk, were fitted with this device, and it should be noted that Catchpole was a millwright in Sudbury, Suffolk. At Tollerton and Hessle Mills, Yorkshire (Plate XIII), the same effect was obtained in a neater manner by inserting two longitudinal shutters end to end in the leading boards of the roller reefing sails.

The annular or circular sail, while best known in connection with modern wind pumps, has also been tried in the old-fashioned grist mills, and four mills have been thus equipped to my knowledge. They were post mills at Feltwell in Norfolk and Roxwell in Suffolk, a smock mill at Boxford (Plate XVI) and a tower mill at Haverhill in Suffolk, which is said to have been the first built with this type of sail in 1860–1 for the owner, Mr. Ruffle, who invented it. All these mills appear to have been so equipped in the 1860's but it is not without significance that Boxford Mill began and ended its days as a normal four-sailed mill. Its history as told to me by one who had worked in it was that the annular sail was put on by Chubbs of Colchester in 1861, and would drive three pairs of stones. On 18th January, 1881, the annular sail was blown off and four patent sails were put up in its place, while the mill was taken down in 1901.

At Haverhill the striking gear of the annular sail was similar to that of a patent sail, and the radial movement of the sail rods was very ingeniously transformed into a more or less tangential movement of the shutter bars; there were one hundred and twenty shutters, five feet long and tapering from twelve and a half to fourteen inches wide, and the wheel was fifty feet in diameter. A governor in the cap regulated the speed of the mill by controlling the shutters. No comparative figures exist as to the efficiency of this type of sail compared with the ordinary patent sail, but I refer the reader to Appendix A on page 185.

To many it may come as a surprise that any windmill should have more than four sails. The earliest record of a multi-sailed mill in England which has come to light up to the present appears to be that of the five-sailed Flint Mill, Leeds, referred to in one of Smeaton's Reports dated 1774, and of which a layout of the sails dated 1758 is among the Smeaton drawings in the Royal Society's library. The chief advantage of a multi-sailed mill is the increase in sail area, with consequent greater driving power; this increase would, of course, be obtained by lengthening or widening the four sails, but lengthening them presented difficulties since the cost does not increase in proportion to the length of the sail, which must be made altogether stouter in order to carry its own weight. When increased width is required much the same trouble arises; moreover, it has been found in practice that the double frame, with sail area on either side of the whip, is not so efficient as the single sail with leading board. An additional advantage in multi-sailed mills is the more even running of the mill. This arises from the fact that when one sail is in the lowest position, shielded from effect of the wind by the mill and doing very little work, there are several sails instead of only one in the position where they can get the maximum amount of wind; in other words a better balance is obtained. Following this argument to its logical conclusion one would imagine that the more sails that could be fitted to a mill the better it would run, but this has been found not to be the case in practice and in addition there is the question of increased cost, and cost of upkeep. The five-sailer has the great disadvantage that when one sail is seriously crippled, the whole mill is put out of action, since it is at once completely out of balance. It cannot have been long after the advent of the five-sailer before the six-sailer was evolved; its advantages over the five-sailer are obvious. If one sail is damaged its opposite number can be removed and the mill worked with four sails set in the form of a St. Andrew's Cross. If in addition another sail becomes damaged, one or two remaining sails can be moved in relation to the rest, and the mill run with three sails. Indeed as a last resource, it can be run with two sails only, and examples of all these sail arrangements on one time six-sailers were to be met with, Metheringham Mill in Lincolnshire having been run with six, four, two and finally three sails. As a point of interest it may be noted that a mill running with two sails is said to give sixty per cent of the power obtained when running with four sails arranged in the usual manner. The eight-sailer is not a favourite in this country, and only seven mills appear to have had eight sails, viz., Wisbech in Cambridgeshire, Much Hadham in Hertfordshire, Diss in Norfolk, Eye near Peterborough (Plate XXII) and Holbeach, Heckington near Sleaford and Rasen in Lincolnshire. Heckington Mill (Plate XIII) has a very curious history; built in 1813 by Tuxford of Boston it was sold when Boston Docks were being made in 1891. The buyer, the late John Pocklington, stripped it of its sails, cap, and all that the tower contained, and re-erected it in the present mill tower at Heckington, which had been built in 1830 by Michael Hare and was later burnt out. The work was extremely well carried out and the five-ton windshaft was lowered, transported and re-erected on successive Saturdays in the snow; but close inspection inside shows that the cap was not built for the present tower. The tips of the sail backs are connected to each other with three-quarter inch diameter iron rods as a strengthening precaution. The mill originally had spring sails, and still drives a pair of stones from a post mill worked by Mr. Pocklington's father. Mr. John Pocklington died in 1943 and the mill ceased to work, only to be bought and repaired as a landmark in 1953 by the Kesteven County Council.

The Lincolnshire type of sail fixing, which is found on the northeast coast and in the counties adjoining Lincolnshire, is well adapted for the use of more than four sails. It is obviously far easier to make a many-armed iron cross to fit the nose of an iron windshaft, than to make an iron windshaft having a poll end to take three or four stocks. Smeaton at first had to devise a special method of fixing five sails since he did not use the cross in the Lincolnshire fashion,[1] and at first used both stocks and a short cross on a four-sailed mill at Wakefield, Yorkshire (Plate IX).

Outside the area of the east Midlands and the north-east, multi-sailed mills have been built here and there in England. Sandhurst in Kent had a five-sailed smock mill, now gone, built by Warrens of Hawkhurst in 1844; they had to send to a firm of millwrights in Lincolnshire for instructions as to how to fix the sails, while Hills of Ashford built a five-sailed pumping mill at Margate which drove a three-throw pump. At Anscombe, Kingston Down, near Lewes, Sussex, there stood a six-sailed post mill which was blown down in 1916, the sails being fixed in a three-way poll end. Peter Payne, a Kentish millwright, fitted a glass neck bearing for the windshaft of this mill; it was removed by Blackman, a Hastings millwright. At Tuttle Hill, near Nuneaton in Warwickshire, there was a five-sailed tower mill which was originally fitted with four sails that almost touched the ground. In 1904, they were so damaged in a storm as to require renewal, but the local council demanded that they should be shortened as they constituted a source of danger by passing very close to the ground. To obtain the same or greater sail area the

[1] *Smeaton's Reports*, Vol. II, p. 396.

millwright, Mr. Blezzard, of Preston in Lancashire, put on five shorter sails in 1905. In Wales there was a five-sailed mill on Parys Mountain, Anglesey, and another called Tan Mill at Llanbadan, Aberystwyth.

Another case in which the local authority took action was at Wisbech in Cambridgeshire, where the fine eight-sailed mill on the Lynn Road had its sails removed as it was considered that it stood too close to the road for safety. The reverse of the case at Tuttle Hill Mill took place at Willingham in Lincolnshire; originally it had six sails but the cross broke and it later ran with four sails on an ordinary four-armed cross. The five-sailed Maud Foster Mill in Skirbeck Quarter, Boston in Lincolnshire (Plate XII) was repaired as a landmark in 1953, with money given to the Society for the Protection of Ancient Buildings by the Reckitt Family Trust. It takes its name from the Maud Foster Drain beside which it stands.

In 1819, Thomas and Isaac Reckitt had the Maud Foster Mill built at Skirbeck on the outskirts of Boston, Lincolnshire, and by the courtesy of Mr. Basil Reckitt I am able to quote the following extracts from his manuscript:

'Mr. Isaac Reckitt's   *Hull, March 19th, 1819.*
Sir,

We undertake to build you a Mill according to plan and Reference and find all materials except brickwork, that is all wood, iron, brasses, millstones, glazier work and labour, all the outside wood work to be painted with 3 coats of paint, the whole to be finished in a good workmanlike manner, and also at our expense convey all the aforesaid materials and fix them according to plan and reference at the spot near Boston Lincolnshire for the sum of Twelve Hundred Pounds.

We are your obedient servants.
Norman & Smithson.

Witness Tho. Petchell.'

In 1823 they put in mills for cement manufacture and a steam engine costing £300. In 1835, a bone mill was added, bones being bought and ground as a fertiliser. A bakehouse had been started in 1821. The partnership accounts were finally closed in 1835 and the mill sold to a Mr. George Cooke of Digby in Lincolnshire. It had been advertised in the *Stamford Mercury* on 16th March, 1835. After a description of the Bone and Cement Mills 'with sixteen horse-power engine' the advertisement reads:

'To be sold by Private Contract, or Let with immediate possession all that newly erected Corn Wind-Mill, seven stories in height, having patent sails that work three pairs of french stones, with an excellent Grannery and drying-kiln sufficient to contain several hundred quarters of wheat, large Dressing and bolting machines, Jumper etc. thereto adjoining and belonging. Also a building used as a bakehouse, attached to the above described premises, with two extensive ovens therein. A Cart shed and a three-stalled stable, and every other requisite convenience for carrying on trade. And also a Paddock or Piece of rich old sward and Pasture Land belonging to the said property, containing by estimation upwards of Two Acres. Mr. Thomas Reckitt, the present occupier, will show the property ; and of the amount of purchase money, rental or other particulars, information may be obtained of the said Thomas Reckitt.'

The subsequent history of the mill can be traced to the present day. George Cooke sold it to Jonathan Dent, who had been negotiating earlier with Thomas Reckitt. Thomas Reynolds was a subsequent miller and then George Spurr (1853–1878). From 1878–1914, a family of the name of Jessop became the owners, followed by Mr. Alfred Ostler; it is now owned by his executors.

The six-sailed mill at Coleby Heath near Lincoln was damaged by fire in the 1860's. Evidently the fire started in the top, for the cap was rebuilt by Rustons of Lincoln with a roof of iron plates, the framing of iron joists and girders; wire rope was used for bracing the steel fan supports, all the gearing was of iron and even the ladder from the dust floor to the cap was of iron. The noise in the cap when the mill was at work is best imagined. It was demolished during the Second World War on account of its proximity to a new airfield. Until 1932, Alford in Lincolnshire possessed the distinction of having a four-sailed, a five-sailed and a six-sailed mill at work in the town, a record only equalled by Horncastle, Lincolnshire, some years since. At the time of writing only Hoyles' five-sailed mill at Alford (Plate XXIV) is at work by wind.

Before leaving the subject of mill sails mention must be made of the little eight-sailed mill which stood on St. Mary's in the Scilly Isles. This mill had *jib sails* similar to those found in the coastal areas of the Iberian Peninsula and round the Mediterranean. There were eight poles, each sail being wrapped round one pole and the end of the jib corded to the next one. The poles were braced to a bowsprit projecting from the front of the windshaft and the whole construction was light and reasonably cheap.

FIG. 44. SHUTTERS OF SAILS: UNION MILL, CRANBROOK

X. WINDING THE MILL

A WINDMILL is designed to work with its sails facing the wind and if a windmill is to work as efficiently as possible its sails must always face the wind squarely; to effect this some means of turning them into the wind, or winding the mill, must be used. The earliest type of turning gear for post, smock and tower windmills was the tail pole, and the earliest method of applying power to it was just bodily force—a man pushing against it. The main steps or ladder of a post mill normally rest on the ground and take some of the thrust of the wind against the mill. To turn the mill into the eye of the wind the miller raised these steps off the ground by means of a lever pivoted on the tail pole (Plate XIV). The front end of the lever is connected to the bottom tread of the ladder by a chain, so that when the other end of the lever is pressed down the ladder which is hinged at the top is raised; the lever is then held down, and the ladder held up, by a loose pin in the side of the tail pole. Very

104

often the miller had a long quant pole in his hands, leant with his back to the tail pole, and pushed hard against the ground with his heels and the quant pole. In this connection Mr. John Bryant, the Colchester millwright, wrote to me: 'Among the thirty-six mills I worked at, there was a variety of methods, but most of the older type used to have a couple of battens fixed to the tail pole wide enough apart for a man to put his head between and shove the mill round by himself. I have done this myself, it is terrible hard work and without a fly tackle the miller has to watch for a change of wind. When I was working at these old mills I used always to bore down to the hole in the crown tree on top of the post and gave it a good drop of oil. One of the millers every winter before the bad weather set in, used to oil like this then get his cob out and harness him to the tail pole and let him pull the mill round about a dozen times, it spared a lot of hard work.' Sometimes the tail pole had a cart wheel fixed to its lower end resting on the ground (Plate XXI) and in such cases, as an alternative to pushing, a horse might be hitched to the pole and made to turn it—or perhaps an ox, when oxen were in common use as draught animals. Or the wheel might have a number of small handles projecting from the side of the rim by which it, and consequently the pole, could be moved by hand. All this is very primitive, and probably at a very early date a number of low posts were set in a circle round the mill and a small winch with a horizontal barrel was built on to the tail pole. A chain or rope was hitched to one of the posts set round the mill and wound on to the barrel, which was turned either by an iron cranked handle or by a wooden wheel having handles like spokes projecting radially from the hub (Plate XV); the drive was generally geared down and this can still be seen at Cat and Fiddle Mill, Dale Abbey, Derbyshire (Plate XXVII). In Holland the tail pole often ends at a gallery running round the mill tower and the rope from the winch is hitched with a grappling hook to one of the slots in the floor of the stage, but in England the only mills seen with this arrangement were the old stone-built tower mill, Deeping St. James, Lincolnshire, and the tower mill built on the ruins of Benets Abbey, Norfolk.

In the case of smock and tower mills the tail pole is braced to the cap by means of two pairs of long braces outside the cap, and in the case of a post mill by means of linked rods to the tail of the mill body.

The Machinery

The introduction of the smock and tower mill opened the way for improvements in winding gear. The first step was to fix a rack to the curb which was built up on top of the body of the mill. The early racks consisted of wooden cogs fixed into the outside face of the curb, though later cast-iron segments of teeth were used; they were geared, through a large wooden worm like a screw attached to the cap, to a wooden chain wheel, its face at right angles to the tower; and over it an endless chain hung down to the ground (Plates IV, IX, XIX and XXII). By pulling the chain, the worm was revolved and moved, with the cap, round the top of the mill tower; this method is still to be seen today but iron worms are also used. The wooden worms were made by setting out the thread on a long strip of paper, which was then pasted round the cylindrical worm blank; the thread was first sawn out and then shaped to the correct profile with a chisel. A variation of this method of turning the cap was to use spur gearing and to place the rack on the top or round the outside of the curb; the wheel in such cases has its face parallel to the mill tower, as can still be seen at Hildenborough Mill, Kent. These racks at first were of wood, but were later of cast iron. The chain wheels are either entirely of wood, of wood with iron Y forks, or all iron including the forks, and the two latter forms are familiarly called Y wheels. This type of winding gear has at one time been in use in most of the windmill districts of England, and it is at present almost the only type found in the western counties.

At Compton Wynyates Mill, Warwickshire, instead of cogs, holes were provided round the curb into which a pin was placed. Two horizontal ungeared winches on either side of the tail of the cap were used to wind up a chain run out to the pin, and thus to turn the cap in either direction. The windmill at Chesterton, Warwickshire (Fig. 37), which started life in 1632 as an observatory, has its cap turned by means of a geared hand winch fixed to the framing inside the cap, the drive being taken through worm and spur reduction gears before it reaches the final spur wheel and rack, a method still used on the Continent, but now unique here.

In 1745, Edmund Lee patented the fantail (Fig. 45 and Plate IV). This consists of what may be considered as a small windmill set at right angles to, and some way behind, the sails of the windmill proper. So long as the wind blows square on to the sails, the fan is presenting no surface to the wind and remains stationary. When the wind changes its direction, it strikes the fan at an angle, and at once sets it in motion. In the case of a smock or tower mill the fan is mounted on a staging fixed to the cap and connected through suitable gearing to the rack on the curb on top of the mill tower (Plate I). The drive may be taken to a worm, or to a spur pinion, as in the case of the chain wheel method. When a spur pinion is used the rack is usually on top of the curb, but it is sometimes fixed on the outer and sometimes on the inner side of the curb also. In most cases the drive is applied at the rear of the cap, that is, as near to the fan as possible; but in a few instances two spur pinions are used, the drive being taken to a kind of differential gear near the centre of the cap, and then divided, one driving pinion being on one side of the cap and the other opposite it. The advantage of this method of drive is that even turning of the cap is ensured by applying the drive to the circular rack at two points opposite one another; a good example was to be seen at Stretham tower mill near Ely, now dismantled, which was built in 1880 on the site of an old post mill and is said to be the last windmill to be built in Cambridgeshire. In all cases provision is made for throwing the fan drive out of gear and turning the cap by hand. When the drive is through a worm there is often a chain wheel with a hand chain hanging down from it outside the cap as at Union Mill, Cranbrook, but when a spur pinion drive is used the drive is either taken through a dog clutch having two or four jaws, through a sliding coupling which can be disconnected and held out of engagement, or through a pinion sliding on its shaft, which is held in or out of gear at will and kept in place by a pin. In this case a square is usually formed on an extended end of a shaft of the driving gear, and an iron key handle is used, sometimes outside on the fan stage.

To apply a fan drive to a post mill five methods were used; in the first (Plates IV, XVIII and XXVIII) an upright wooden carriage running on two tandem iron wheels, and consisting of two upright stays with horizontal cross members and diagonal braces, was mounted on the end of the tail pole and suitably braced to it. The fan was mounted on a horizontal shaft at the top of this carriage and the drive taken down to the bottom, where it divided and drove the two wheels by means of geared rings fixed to the sides of the wheels, or each wheel might be separately driven from the fan shaft. A track was provided round the mill on which these wheels could run and so turn the whole mill body. Elm or oak slabs were sometimes laid down, and an earth track had usually a well-drained foundation of chalk and flint; the commonest and best track was one of well-rolled gravel. This method of fan drive was used in the southern counties, as at Argos Hill and Cross in Hand Mills in Sussex, and isolated examples were to be found elsewhere as at Tottenhill in Norfolk and at Chinnor in Oxfordshire.

In East Anglia, however, and in Suffolk in particular, the tail pole was cut off at the point where it projected through the ladder (Plates XXIII, XXVII and XXVIII), or was removed altogether, and the carriage wheels were mounted on the end of the ladder, the

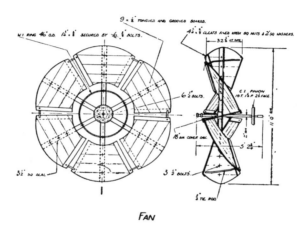

FAN

FIG. 45. FAN, FORNCETT END MILL, NORFOLK

wheels being driven in the same way or with two vertical shafts from the fan shaft as at Great Chishill, Cambridgeshire. The advantage of this method of mounting was said to be that the carriage and fan were better supported, and being closer into the body of the mill there was not so much tendency for the fan to act as a weather vane and to sway the mill in an unsteady wind. Against this it was argued that with the Sussex-type fantail the fan caught the wind more readily, being mounted further out and not shielded from the wind by the body of the mill, and in addition for the same reason turned the mill closer into the eye of the wind than the Suffolk fan. Without working data of mills with both types of fantail it is not possible to give a preference, but structurally the Suffolk fantail was undoubtedly the best. In addition to Tuxford composite mill the post mill at Happisburgh, Norfolk, and Eld's tower mill, Coventry, Warwickshire (Plate XX), had twin fans, which undoubtedly kept the sails closer into the eye of the wind than one fantail could.

A third type of fan drive for post mills was that in which the fan was mounted on the roof of the mill and the drive taken down to a worm ring fixed to the post just below the mill body. This drive could be seen in operation at the mill at Ramsey in Essex, built in 1842 by Whitmore and Binyon of Wickham Market in Suffolk, and was formerly used on the post mill at Swilland in Suffolk, which now has the ordinary Suffolk type of fantail, and in several mills now gone.

The fourth type of drive was from a fan on the roof down to wheels on the bottom of the ladder as at Stanton Chair Mill, Suffolk, Hogg Hill Mill, Icklesham, Udimore Mill and other mills in Sussex, and the fifth was a drive down from the roof to a rack on top of the roundhouse as at Lower Dean, Bedfordshire.

A fan consists of an iron hub mounted on a horizontal, square iron shaft; into the sockets in the hub are fitted square wooden spokes, the outer half being cut at an angle to the shaft. On these outer halves of the spokes are mounted the fan blades, shaped like segments of a ring, built up horizontally of a number of pieces of flat boarding strengthened at the edges with wooden battens on one side only. Iron rods connect the tips of adjacent blades in order to stiffen the whole assembly and sometimes two iron rings are fixed to the spokes inside the fan blades. As a rule fans have six or eight blades and the former have sometimes been painted red, white and blue by millers in the past. In the south, five-bladed fans as at Polegate tower mill, and ten-bladed fans as at Udimore post mill, both in Sussex, were sometimes found; but the seven-bladed fans on the smock mills at Hatfield Peverel, Essex, and Kingsdown in Kent and on the drainage mill at Horning Ferry, Norfolk, were unusual, and it is difficult to imagine why that particular number was chosen. Kingsdown Mill is said to have been moved from Farningham to its present position in about 1880 and it is now derelict. The four-bladed fan on Behag's Mill at Worboys, Huntingdonshire, was probably an eight-bladed fan with four blades missing.

The fantail has not been adopted abroad to any extent except in Denmark, where it is claimed to have been introduced by Englands, a firm of Norfolk millwrights, in Germany and in the Provinces of

Friesland and Groningen in the Netherlands. In all these areas patent sails are also used.

It will be seen that a fan is practically automatic, and provided that all is in order it only fails to function in a thunderstorm (Fig. 46). As a storm of this kind moves across the country in a straight line like a wave curling back on itself, the hot air in front of it flows in from the opposite direction, rising to meet the storm. At any point just in front of this line of advance of the storm, therefore, the wind, which will have been blowing in the opposite direction to the storm, will drop and, as the storm sweeps over the spot, will suddenly blow strongly from the opposite direction. This does not give the fantail of a mill a chance of turning the sails through

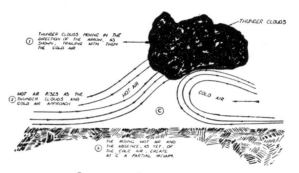

FIG. 46. THE LULL BEFORE THE STORM
Diagrammatical explanation of the proverbial saying.

one hundred and eighty degrees to face the new direction in time, and in such a case the miller must turn the cap or the mill by hand or it will become tail-winded; the cloths or shutters will be blown out of the sails and possibly the mill will be blown over forwards in the case of a post mill, or the cap blown off in the case of a tower mill. By quartering the mill (i.e. turning the sails through ninety degrees) the edge of the sails will be presented to the wind and heavy gales have been withstood without serious damage in this way.

In 1891, Dick Blezzard the millwright of Preston, Lancashire, was at Singleton tower mill when it became tail-winded; the cap was lifted off and a sail was smashed. In the freak storm at the end of July, 1946, Syleham post mill, Suffolk (Plate XXII), was tail-winded and Mr. Jack Penton, who then owned it, sent me the following vivid account of what happened.

Winding the Mill

'On that Friday afternoon the mill was facing south-east and several thunderstorms had passed by quite safely. At about 6 p.m. a really frightful cloud appeared in the south-west. I was a little bit anxious about the mill and went out to crank the fly so that the mill faced the south and the fly would catch the wind from the storm. Just as I was about to do this a strong wind from the north-east arose and took the ladder to the foot of the engine house, and I was completely unable to move the mill out of this highly dangerous position. Meanwhile it was nearly dark and I was about to climb out on the fly staging when the wind suddenly stopped and before I could reach the bottom of the ladder a terrific blast of wind and hail struck us from the south-west. The sails started off backwards and above the din I heard a bang and found the striking rod had snapped off the cross iron, and vanes jammed shut and there was nothing else I could do but rush into the mill and lighten off the tail runner stone which was making a deafening noise and shaking the mill to bits. While I was doing this, with a frightful crash the crotch spindle jumped out and away went the sails at a speed I can hardly bear to think of now. Needless to say I dashed full tilt down the ladder and into the house to await what I felt *certain* would be the total destruction of the mill. Fairly soon the fly took the mill round into the storm and with the vanes still jammed she set off forwards and though I could only *just* see the mill through the haze and hail, she was turning over in a slow halting way. When at last the tempest ended I found the windshaft pulled about eight inches forward and the chair block slipped slanting across the weather-beam and hanging right over the edge!—a horrible sight, not to mention the chaos caused by the tail wheel's journey forward. The sails were only slightly damaged and the main timbers of the buck remained unmoved! Thank Heaven! I had a sound weather-beam. . . .

'With a pulley block from the windshaft at the tail wheel to the floor joists and a lateral pull from the windshaft at the head wheel to the tailbeam we slowly and surely pulled her back into place. Only afterwards did we agree what a highly unpleasant job it was! Of course I forgot to say, before moving her into the house we took the neck up off the brass and so there were three points to watch with the very keenest interest!'

Fans are geared very low; typical mills such as the tower mill at Kenninghall and the post mill at Sprowston, both in Norfolk, required 1170 and 625 revolutions of the fan, respectively, to turn the sails in a full circle. At 120 r.p.m. this means five minutes, or two and a half minutes to turn through the half-circle.

At Billingford in Norfolk (Plate XXV) a tower mill stands on the site of an old post mill which was tail-winded in a storm in 1860 and blown over forwards while the miller was actually in it attending to the stones. He was saved from being crushed by the stout post which held the broken debris off him, and he escaped with cuts and bruises; but a man who was descending the ladder at the back fell into the wreckage and was so badly injured that he died.

Under ordinary circumstances the automatic fantail relieves the miller of much trouble in observing the direction of the wind, and it must be regarded as one of the factors that have caused windmills to survive as long as they have in such a highly industrialised country as England.

FIG. 47. FANTAIL, UNION MILL, CRANBROOK

XI. CAPS

THE cap of a windmill consists of a horizontal framework on which are erected spars or rafters, forming the framework of the roof, which is then covered with suitable material. Not only do caps vary in size and shape, but the cap bases vary considerably in construction and in nomenclature according to local practice, and only a brief outline description of typical caps can be attempted here.

In the majority of cases two long beams called sheer trees or sheers, about twelve inches square, run fore and aft on either side of the cap, and are connected by various beams, some of which act as stays only, while others perform additional functions. The front or neck bearing assembly of the windshaft rests on a beam connecting the two sheers in the front and known as the rode balk, weather beam or breast beam, the bearing assembly being held in place on it by vertical neck studs. At the centre of the cap frame is the sprattle beam or centre beam, which carries the top bearing of the upright shaft. Behind this is usually the tail beam of about the same size which carries the tail bearing and thrust block of the windshaft. In some cases the tail beam is dispensed with and two joists connecting the sprattle beam together with a tail end tie beam carry a tail block, which takes the tail bearing and can be adjusted in its mortises by wedges. In cases where the sheers project behind the cap to carry the fan they are connected at their ends by a cap piece, while if a fan stage is required the sheers project still further and two joists between them carry boards which form a platform. So much for the frame. This has to turn on the curb or track, which is built on top of the tower, and for this purpose a substructure or cap circle is often built and fixed to the bottom of the frame. It consists of from five to eight pieces of wood braced to each sheer by a joist or puncheon, and sometimes by a couple of intermediate joists in addition. This cap circle carries the rollers, blocks, or a track, which form the bearing surface when the cap moves round. In some cases two breast cap sills under the breast beam and two more sills at about forty-five degrees to the sheers in the tail are used instead of a cap circle, much depending on the shape of the cap.

The cap superstructure is built up on the cap circle, if there is one, and on the frame if there is not. As a rule it consists of spars or rafters often braced in between with horizontal girts. On top of these is laid boarding, the outer covering on top of this, if any, varying according to local custom. A storm hatch is provided above the windshaft in the breast for access to the sails, and as a rule a door is provided in the tail in addition, or failing this usually another hatch.

If a fan is fitted it is supported by fly spars or fan uprights varying from fully vertical to perhaps thirty degrees to the horizontal, but in all cases mortised to the sheers, and braced to them and sometimes to the cap itself by various spurns, fan braces, tie beams or stays. Iron rollers run on a cast-iron curb or on a wooden curb which has an iron track on top. The rollers, which vary in size, are placed so as to take the weight most effectively, two or three spaced out on each side. Sometimes they run on iron pins and are let into the cap circle, and sometimes the pins themselves turn in eye bearings; a mill with rollers in the cap is said to have a live curb. An alternative method is to use blocks of wood or gun metal instead of rollers, and in some cases the blocks are fixed to the curb and the track is on the base of the cap circle; a mill with blocks instead of rollers is said to have a dead curb, and a few mills in Norfolk have a dead curb with rollers in front under the breast beam only. Distinct from either of these types is the shot curb; in this type a special track is fixed to the bottom of the cap circle as well as the top of the curb, and between the two tracks are a number of rollers evenly pitched all the way round and held between an outer and inner built-up iron ring, thus forming a type of roller thrust bearing.

To centre the cap iron sheaves, truckles or truck wheels running on vertical pins against the side of the curb proper are fixed to the bottom of the cap frame, occasionally two being mounted on the same pin. In some cases wooden blocks are used instead and in the case of smock mills the tops of the corner posts may serve, whilst in others the blocks or rollers on which the cap turns do double duty and take the side thrust as well. Frequently these truck wheels run under a keep flange, which forms part of the curb; and this prevents any tendency of the cap to lift off the curb should the mill be tail-winded. In Anglesey, Wirral and the Lancashire Fylde, a cap centring frame, called the well frame, peculiar to those parts, was to be found (Fig. 48). Four upright corner posts, suitably braced and holding a horizontal frame a few inches clear of the dust floor, were hung down from the cap sheers, and a flanged iron ring was fixed to two joists of the dust floor and projected upwards through the floor boarding and into a hole in the centre of the frame. The whole affair looked something like an oblong table hung upside-down, with a large short drainpipe stuck up from below into a hole in the middle of it. The frame fitted closely round the ring and in this way only a truly circular movement of the cap was permitted. The size of the framing varied with the size of the mill; at Melin y Bont, Bryn-dû, in Anglesey, it was about nine feet long, five feet wide and five feet deep, while the ring was about three feet in diameter and seven

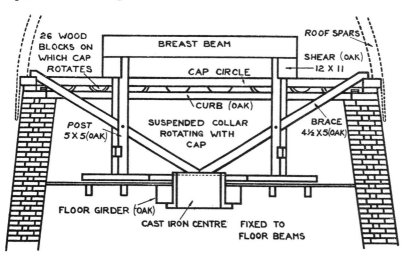

FIG. 48. CAP CENTRING FRAME, ANGLESEY

inches deep. The ladder into the cap was fixed to the framing clear of the floor and revolved with it.

Many mills have come to a stop because the tower and hence the curb distorted, and the fan drive could no longer turn the cap all the way round. To obviate this at Swavesey tower mill, Cambridgeshire, and in some other mills a gap was left between the top of the tower and the bottom of the curb, which was filled with a large number of wedges, and by adjusting these wedges the curb could be kept true. The sinking of brick towers to one side was a fairly common occurrence and millwrights jacked them up and underpinned them when this occurred, Burgh-le-Marsh five-sailed mill, Lincolnshire, being a good example (Plate XXIV). Towers often cracked for the same reason and iron bands in several places were put round them to strengthen them in such cases as at Stansted, Essex, the last bolt holding each band being put in red hot, so that on cooling its contraction tightened the band.

The boarding of caps is often double, the outer layer overlapping the joints of the inner layer, and sometimes projecting to as much as two feet below the top of the curb to form a petticoat, the bottom of which was nicely scalloped in true feminine style in some cases. In the case of ogee caps with longitudinal boarding, the curved cap spars are in two pieces, top and bottom, meeting at a wooden ring at the joining of the two curves which are usually approximately equal in radius and the inner layer of boarding is usually horizontal. Shingles at Crosby Mill, Liverpool, thatch at High Ham Mill, Somerset, copper at Blackthorne Mill, Oxfordshire, lead at Chesterton Mill, Warwickshire, and iron plates at Tuttle Hill Mill, Nuneaton, Warwickshire, are various types of covering of caps. A very favourite method was to cover the boarding of the cap with canvas, well saturated with white lead paint, which held it on and made it waterproof. Galleries round caps were to be found only in certain parts of the country apart from isolated examples, the chief districts being Norfolk, Suffolk, Cambridgeshire, Bedfordshire and Hertfordshire. Their advantage was that it was easy to work on the cap or the head of the windshaft, and obtain access to the sails when necessary; their disadvantage, that they disturbed the flow of air from behind the sails. They could also cause uncomfortable moments, as was found when examining Eye tower mill, Peterborough (Plate XXIII). Having walked round the gallery to the sails and taken some measurements of the cross and striking gear, I saw, when starting to return, that the bearers carrying the gallery were all extremely rotten, and one had rotted right through. It was not possible to open the storm hatch from the outside, nor to attract the owner's attention, so that the only thing to do was to walk back again with an extremely uncomfortable feeling and the resolve to be more careful in future. Mr. T. B. Hunt, the Soham millwright, told me that his uncle fell from the fan stage of a mill cap forty feet and through the roof of an out-building below. He was a 'hard man' for he not only lived to tell the tale, but he actually walked home.

A certain amount of decoration of caps is indulged in besides the scalloped petticoat. Finials in the shape of an acorn or some other

Caps

fancy shape are to be found frequently on pepper-pot caps, while the ogee cap is usually surmounted by a knob, and the cap of Arrington Mill, Cambridgeshire, was painted in broad segments, red, white and blue. Curious caps are to be met with up and down the country. At Stansted Mountfitchet, Essex, where the windmill has been repaired as a landmark, it is not possible to reach the fan from the rear of the cap in the ordinary way; instead a hatch is fixed over an oval hole in the top of the cap and a special small portable ladder, made to suit the curve of the cap, is provided to reach the fan. Pride of place for the largest existing cap in England, and perhaps elsewhere, must surely go to Old Buckenham Mill, Norfolk, built for J. J. Colman of mustard fame in 1818 and now derelict (Plate III). The tapering boat-shaped cap is twenty-three feet from front to rear, twenty-one feet from side to side, and fourteen feet high above the sprattle beam—the sizes being taken from the inside of the cap spars at the level of the cap frame. This cap has a hatch above the brake wheel in addition to the usual rear door, for ease of access to the top when painting or repairing. Caps were usually typical of the areas in which mills stood. The ogee caps of the east Midlands and north-east varied considerably (Plates XVII, XXIV, XXVI and XXVIII), some having a reverse curve inwards at the bottom, others not, some fan frames having a lattice-braced hand rail, others being plain, and even the ball finials varying according to the tradition of the firm of millwrights that built the mill. The boat-shaped caps of the north-west varied too in Lancashire, Cheshire and Anglesey (Plates IV, XXI and XXVIII); while the more pleasing boat-shaped cap of Norfolk (Plates II and XXV), which Englands, the millwrights, claimed to have introduced, replaced a round dome-shaped cap, an example of which still survives on Blakeney tower mill. The ogee caps of the King's Lynn area were quite distinctive and often had light iron galleries round them. In Cambridgeshire there was a type of cap, dome-shaped, with the fan frame braced to the top of it, which originated in Soham and spread north and south through the county; while another type of pepper-pot shape with an acorn finial, though peculiar to the Suffolk-Cambridgeshire border, seems to have been the original of similar caps in Essex. The post mill type of Kentish cap crossed the Thames into Essex and went south and west into Sussex, while the mills round Chichester, West Sussex, had their own tradition of dome-shaped caps.

To be efficient a cap should disturb the air flow behind the sails as little as possible; all other factors being equal, the rounded caps are the best, such as the Norfolk boat-shaped with curved ridge and sides, the Lincolnshire ogee, the hemispherical, and the conical. The squarer types with bluff fronts such as the Kentish post mill roof type, the pent roof, the tapering boat-shaped and the horizontal ridge boat-shaped are bad. The fan supports are best placed well behind the cap and low down, as found in Norfolk, as they may easily spoil the best of caps from the point of view of air flow, as in the Lincolnshire type.

XII. WINDSHAFTS

THE windshaft is the axle of the sails. It revolves in the top of the windmill and is tilted up at an angle to the horizontal, which varies from five to fifteen degrees, in order that a proportion of the weight of the sails, which are very heavy indeed, may be transferred to the bearing at the tail of the windshaft. This also takes the force of the thrust of the wind against the sails and is called the thrust bearing.

The early windshafts were of wood, and the stocks of the sails were mortised through them as in the windshaft from Thornham composite mill, Norfolk, now in the Bridewell Museum, Norwich. This arrangement can still be seen in use abroad; in England, however, most of the few remaining wooden windshafts have had their front ends cut off and an iron poll end put on to carry the sails. But by far the greater number of English windshafts are made of cast iron (Plate XVII); this practice was introduced by John Smeaton in 1754 and he was responsible for the introduction of cast iron generally into windmill work. In the south, east and Midlands the iron windshaft has a poll end to carry the sails; this is a double box with openings at right angles, through which the sail stocks are passed and then fixed in place by wedges or pinch screws, and it is a similar poll end which is fitted to the old wooden windshafts and held in place with iron bands; both these examples are to be met with abroad. In Lincolnshire and the north-east a different method is favoured; on the end of the cast-iron windshaft is hung, with iron wedges or keys, a heavy cast-iron cross (Plate XVI), with arms well ribbed, which have sundry holes cast in and two bosses projecting on each side. Sail stocks are dispensed with, the whips or backbones of the sails made stouter, lengthened and called backs and held to the front of the arms of the cross with iron clamps and bolts. In the west a similar method was adopted, but very often sail stocks were used in halves; the whips in front of them and wood clamps called counter backs in front of the cross and behind the stocks to strengthen them; and sometimes a light plate iron cross was fixed in front of the whips for the same purpose. The iron crosses are of large dimensions and like the poll ends extremely heavy; an average spread of the arms of such a cross would be thirteen feet, with a width of ten inches, while an average central boss from which these arms radiate would be four feet in diameter and twelve inches thick. Sail backs average ten inches square, tapering outwards to about five inches square, and thirty-five feet long or more.

A wooden windshaft was often of great size, twenty four inches in diameter being met with. In England these shafts were of oak and were often octagonal, tapering down from neck to tail. Iron wind-shafts were naturally smaller, they were most usually round, and ten inches in diameter. In Norfolk they were often made in two parts for ease of erection, the parts being bolted together with a flanged coupling near the tail. Lengths varied greatly and very short and light shafts had to be fitted with a heavy counterweight near the tail in order to balance the weight of the sails; an example of this could be seen at Stretham Mill on the Cambridge–Ely road.

The neck journal bearings in the front of the windshaft present no difficulty when the windshaft is of iron, but in the case of wooden windshafts a good wearing surface was obtained by letting a number of strips of wrought iron into the portion of the shaft at the neck made round for the purpose. At Upminster Mill in Essex and at South Ockenden Mill nearby, alternate wood and iron strips were fitted to the iron windshafts to increase the diameter of the neck. The wrought-iron strips were one inch square, separated by wooden strips half an inch wide and held on to the shaft by two iron clips, being prevented from moving by the poll end in front and a clamp behind.

The tail of a wooden windshaft is fitted with an iron pintle or gudgeon which takes the thrust and axial loads, though in the older

The Machinery

mills a separate journal was provided also, similar to the neck journal but smaller. With a cast-iron shaft the thrust and axial loads are taken in one combined housing, often having a good gun-metal (brass) thrust block. On occasion the thrust was taken from a flange on the end of the shaft on to a wooden pad, and one such pad, found when the old composite mill at Thornham in Norfolk collapsed, has been proved to be of beech.

The material of the first windshaft bearings was probably stone; even now it is used abroad and can be found here and there in England as at Cat and Fiddle post mill, Dale Abbey, Derbyshire. The neck bearing from Thornham Mill, Norfolk, is also in the Bridewell Museum. It is roughly shaped blue marble let into an oak block and secured by lead and plaster. The working surface, however, is beautifully smooth and polished and obviously has a low coefficient of friction; the journal carried by this bearing was alternately wood and iron. Flint and Nottingham block have been used and the glass bearing in Kingston Downs Mill, Sussex, has already been mentioned; but a neck bearing smothered in black grease is one of the most difficult parts of the mill to examine *in situ*. The neck bearing at Thornton Mill in Lancashire was at one time a kind of red granite; and Dick Blezzard told me that in the old days, it is said, a miller was allowed by law to take up any cobble stone in any yard if it was suitable for a bearing. Hard woods were used too, lignum vitae—as one would expect—oak, thorn, elm and other woods also, but a hard brass or gun metal were the most common. These were usually cast by the millwright, and old brass clock faces, candlesticks, and pestles and mortars were often melted down in the past for this purpose, as many old millwrights could tell. One successful type of neck bearing used in East Anglia consisted of a shaped oak block into which was let a square gun-metal bar set cornerways to the line of the windshaft. The top was shaped to suit the radius of the journal and the bar was supported by folding wedges at the bottom, about one-sixteenth of an inch projecting through the oak block. As the brass wore away the wedges were driven up, and when the limit of adjustment was reached the shaft was jacked up and packing put under the wedges, the process being repeated until the brass had worn down to the thickness of the bottom of the oak block. Another East Anglian type of bearing was called the swing pot, the bearing housing having trunnions at right angles to the

ix. Oil mill built at Wakefield, Yorkshire, by John Smeaton, 1755.

x. Sir William Cubitt.

XI. Holograph drawing by Sir William Cubitt showing his patent
sails, 1823.

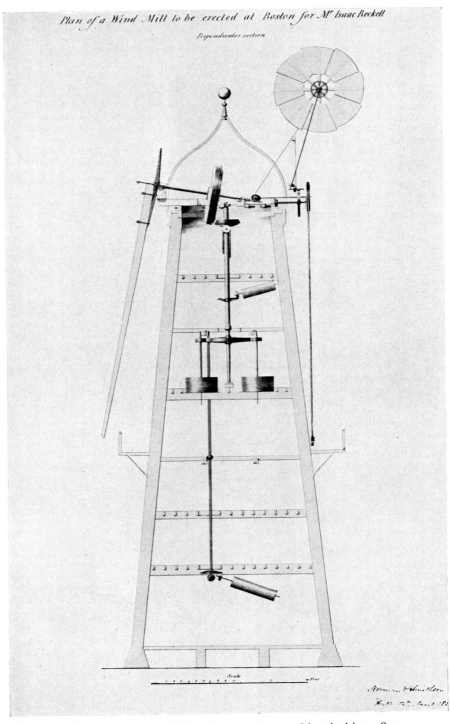

XII. The Maud Foster Mill, Skirbeck, Boston, Lincolnshire, 1819.

XIIIa. Hessle Mill, near Hull, Yorkshire, with roller reefing sails and 'air brakes'.

XIIIb. Heckington Mill, Lincolnshire, built at Boston 1813, moved 1891, now preserved.

xiv. Post mill at Millwall, London, by Miss H. J. J. West, *c.* 1830.

xv*a*. Penny Hill smock mill, Lincolnshire, 1832, by Hilkiah Burgess.

xv*b*. North Drain, Deeping Fen, Lincolnshire, 1828, by H. Burgess.

XVI. Boxford Mill, Suffolk, built 1841, fitted with an annular sail 1861, demolished 1901.

axis of the bearing, which rendered it self-aligning. At a mill at Barton-on-Humber in Lincolnshire a roller bearing with five rollers, the patent of a Mr. Sutton, was tried. It proved unsuccessful owing to the crumbling of the surface of the cast iron at the windshaft neck journal. A roller bearing with three rollers was put in Upper Hellesdon Mill, Norwich; it is said that it cut through a cast-iron shaft in six weeks and a cast-steel shaft was afterwards fitted. Jacks were used to raise the windshafts, their capacity being about five tons. These were often entirely of wood, except for the iron bands round the screw heads, and were cut with a screw box in the same way as were bench screws. These screw boxes were obviously home-made, the helix being apparently set out in the time-honoured way with paper, and there were improvised guides (they cannot be called nuts) to feed them into the work. Most of the old country millwrights undertook to cut wooden screws; Mr. Horton of Hythe used to possess a board, once the property of a local millwright, on which, amongst other things, was advertised 'Wooden screws cut to order'.

In post mills as in tower mills, the neck and tail bearings are carried by the breast and tail beams, respectively. In the case of Sprowston Mill, Norwich, burned down in 1933, these beams were carried on a sub-frame in the top of the mill, and by means of a screw this whole assembly, which carried the windshaft and sails as well, could be moved forwards or backwards in relation to the main frame of the mill body. This was actually done by the miller when he found that the sails by reason of wear in the bearings were just touching the roof of the roundhouse, and the operation was termed putting the sails out of house.

XIII. BRAKE WHEELS, BRAKES AND WALLOWERS

THE brake wheel, sometimes known as the head wheel, is so called from the fact that the brake, which stops the mill, acts on the rim. In the earliest type two and sometimes three arms were mortised through and wedged into the wooden windshaft and the wheel was completed by the addition of four, six or eight cants and a sectional rim into which the wooden cogs were fixed. This is known as the compass arm wheel and is essentially a weak construction, since the mortises weaken the shaft at the very spot where strength is most needed; it is in addition very difficult to true up. The type of wheel known as the clasp arm or griped arm is almost universal in England today so far as wooden wheels are concerned, and must have been introduced in about the first quarter of the eighteenth century, as there are no dated wheels or illustrations of them before that period. As its name implies its four arms clasp the windshaft, which is contained in the square thus formed at the centre. The actual fixing to an iron windshaft is either—

(a) On a wooden square built up on a square on the windshaft.

(b) On four horns or on ribs cast on the windshaft.

(c) On a square iron box hung on the shaft with wedges.

Both the arms, the cants and the rim are often doubled and the whole construction is immensely strong.

The construction of a wooden clasp arm wheel allows easy dismantling and erection, a particularly great advantage in earlier times, and it is staked or hung on to its shaft with wedges, usually four at each corner, which permits easy truing up. Oak was most commonly used for all these wheels, although wheels of elm, beech and hornbeam were to be found.

A later type of brake wheel, found on iron windshafts only, had an iron boss and spokes with a wooden rim built upon it. The iron portion was split diametrically and bolted up in position, the fixing to the shaft being by wedges; a curious brake wheel at Barrington tower mill, Cambridgeshire, had an iron hub with eight wooden radial arms.

John Smeaton was the first to use large cast-iron gears in the water-driven Carron Rolling Mill in 1754, and brake wheels entirely of iron are also used, either with the rims cast solid with the spokes and boss, or cast separately and bolted on. Brake wheels vary greatly in size—six feet was about the smallest and eleven feet six inches about the largest noted, the latter being at Diss tower mill in Norfolk. In post mills the brake wheel is mounted forward on the windshaft not far behind the neck journal; but in tower mills it is further back, as it has to gear with the wallower, which is in the exact centre of the cap. The teeth of these brake wheels, which are practically face gears, were originally, and often still are, all of wood; the cogs were sawn roughly to shape in wooden jigs or boxes, the shanks shaped up by hand and the cogs fitted into the mortises in the wheel. They were then turned up true and marked out and pared with a chisel to the correct profile. The shanks projected through the rim and were held at the back with wood or iron pins driven through radially to the wheel; sometimes wedges were driven up tight between dovetailed shanks, while a few survive with the shanks split and small forged iron wedges driven in to swell the shanks to a tight fit into the mortises of the wheel, as at Tadworth post mill, Surrey. In this connection Mr. Russell of Cranbrook writes as follows: 'I helped a man named George Harmer (he worked for years for Hill of Ashford) gear a large spur wheel at Wateringbury. He used his compasses with very obtuse points, about as you would grind a centre punch and said the points did not sink into the wood. Warren (the Hawkhurst millwright) thought it most extraordinary and had never heard of such goings on. Harmer had a semi-sacred chisel kept for cog-paring only. He kept it in the bottom of his tool chest wrapped in greased cloth when not in use. He was a very neat workman. I had to face the backs of the cogs while he did the driving or front side. I remember the cog pit was very draughty and the weather very cold. The old cogs had been in so long they were spongy behind and burred up under the hammer. We had to mortise most of them out, which took several days.'

All kinds of wood were used, apple, pear, oak, hornbeam, thorn, holly, beech and others beside. The tougher the wood the better, provided it could be easily worked, and where they were easily obtainable crab apple and hornbeam were favourites, owing to their resilience and close grain. Millwrights were said to purchase Blenheim Orange trees for cog making since these were the largest of the apple trees. To lubricate the teeth while running, grease or linseed oil was used and Mr. Russell used to soak new cogs in linseed oil before fitting; as a lubricant grease was the more common and where the wooden cogs meshed with iron teeth it was essential; but if wood ran with wood, linseed oil was preferable (though seldom used) and under good conditions a set of cogs would literally last half a lifetime. Several sets known to me worked for over forty years, an example being at Gislingham tower mill, Suffolk. When once run in under such circumstances, they attained a high polish and their quietness was almost unbelievable. In some post mills two rows of cogs were fitted to the brake wheel as at Friston Mill, Suffolk, the inner row to drive the machinery and the outer row for the drive to the stones. In the mill moved from Ellington, Huntingdonshire, and re-erected at Madingley, Cambridgeshire, the brake wheel and wallower have two rows of staggered cogs, evidently to avoid backlash.

In place of wooden cogs, however, iron teeth cast in segments were often used, but in such cases more often than not they meshed with wooden cogs. This was common practice in Suffolk, where the segments were bolted to the face of the clasp arm wheels, replacing the wooden cogs which had been previously sawn off flush. The most curious teeth were to be seen at Peasenhall post mill, Suffolk, where the brake wheel had hypoid teeth cast in segments. These were made necessary by the fact that on the upright shaft the straight-toothed wallower, which gears with the brake wheel, was mounted off-centre in order to accommodate two pairs of stones of somewhat unequal size.

In England the most usual type of brake or gripe was a thick elm band in six or eight lengths held together with iron plates and bolts and extending round the brake wheel, one end being anchored on one side and the other attached to the brake lever on the same side. The lever itself was a heavy beam, varying in section and length, which of its own weight held the brake on. To release the brake the lever was raised by means of a rope running over a pulley above the lever and usually down to some position from which the sails could be seen easily, so that they could be brought to rest in the desired position. The lever was held up in the 'off' position by a swinging catch, having a slot into which a pin on the lever fell, and to release it again and apply the brake it was only necessary to pull the brake rope, thus raising the lever and allowing the catch to swing free. It will thus be seen that those old millwrights understood the first principles of safety first since the brake is normally 'on' and has to be pulled 'off'. In some Sussex mills, of which Patcham tower mill is an example, the brake was put on by a handle and a screw driving bevel gears, but this practice does not seem to have found favour elsewhere. In some cases the brake lever was of iron, and as an alternative to a sectional wooden band for the brake, an iron band either in sections or whole was often used, and sometimes this was faced with wooden blocks. In some of the drainage mills on the Norfolk Broads, as for example at Stracy Arms Mill, Tunstall, the brake consisted of small rectangular wood blocks threaded over a three-quarter inch square iron rod and backed with a strip of hoop iron.

Sometimes mills ran away in a storm and could not be stopped with the brake for fear of setting fire to it. In such cases the miller tried to quarter the mill, by turning the sails edgewise to the wind, to choke the stones with grain and thus pull the mill up, or to ride out the storm giving the stones as much work as they could do.

The wallower is the term given to the wheel directly driven by the brake wheel and in England is behind it, but abroad is sometimes found in front of it. Bevel gears were first worked out by Camus in 1752 together with the properties of cycloidal teeth; before that time face gears, trundle wheels and lantern pinions were used. The first wallowers were lantern pinions and one is still to be seen in Chesterton tower mill, Warwickshire (Fig. 37). The staves of the lantern pinion were fixed top and bottom into two roundels or flanges, sometimes by pins and sometimes by wedges driven into the ends to swell them out in the same way as a hammer handle is fixed to its head; and when worn they could be turned round and the pinion moved up or down on its spindle so as to get a fresh wearing surface without weakening the staves unduly. The next type of wallower was the pin gear known also as the trundle or cow-pop gear, which was something like a lantern pinion without a top flange, but with a larger number of shorter staves; in this case the staves were often wooden sleeves mounted on iron spindles. The most usual type of wallower was in effect a bevel wheel of wood or iron, with all the variations associated with brake wheels. Iron wheels with or without wooden cogs were as much favoured as wooden wheels, which were sometimes solid as at Herne Mill, Kent.

XIV. THE FINAL DRIVE TO THE STONES

I N post mills (Fig. 13), direct drive to the stones from the brake wheel in the breast, and the tail wheel (if there was one) in the tail, preceded the more complicated indirect drive through a wallower and upright shaft. In tower mills in England none survive with direct drive from the brake wheel to the stones as can still be found abroad, and the upright shaft and wallower are invariable. In the case of post mills upright shafts were mainly used in the breast only as at Saxtead Green Mill, but were sometimes to be found in the tail as well, as in the case of Friston Mill, Suffolk. Originally such shafts were of wood and one such shaft still survives at Tilbrook Mill, Huntingdonshire, but the majority were of iron. In tower mills, however, both wood and iron shafts were to be found and some had a section of each material and were called graft shafts.

In most tower mills (Fig. 27) the upright shaft was in two or more sections connected with a dog-clutch type of coupling, which enabled the long shaft to be installed more easily than if it was in one piece. The bearing at the top of the shaft was a plain journal bearing on the side of the centre beam in the cap of a tower mill, or on a horizontal spindle beam between the two upper side girts in the case of a post mill. There was usually an intermediate bearing to prevent whip in the shaft, and the combined journal and thrust bearing at the bottom of the shaft was originally a brass pot bearing let into a sprattle beam mortised into two horizontal timbers at right angles to it, as can still be seen at Cranbrook Mill. Folding wedges were used to adjust the position of the sprattle itself in two directions, to get the lower bearing of the upright shaft truly in line with the upper bearing in the cap, and of course on the exact centre line of the mill; otherwise the cap could not be turned, because the brake wheel and wallower would be too close in mesh at one point. This laborious method was largely superseded by the cast-iron bridging-box with four adjusting screws for the bearing.

The wooden upright shafts of oak, pine, elm or other tough timber varied in size up to about eighteen inches square, and in shape varied from square through octagonal and sixteen-sided to round. A very fine example of a sixteen-sided shaft with interesting decorative stop chamfers and carrying a massive great spur wheel still exists at Damgate Mill, Holbeach, Lincolnshire, and there is another fine one at Little Cressingham Mill, Norfolk. Iron shafts, usually round or square, were about one-third the size of wooden ones and in Lincolnshire the lowest section was frequently only the height of one floor, as at Trader Mill, Sibsey. Before Duloe Mill, Eaton Socon, Bedfordshire, was turned into a house I was one day struck by the small size of the lowest section of the upright shaft, which looked as though it had been made from a five-inch sapling. Examination showed that it was not wood at all but iron, the millwrights having used a straight piece of willow as a pattern in the foundry; the patterning of the bark had, of course, been reproduced in the sand and consequently on the casting.

The great spur wheel is mounted on the upright shaft and drives the stones through pinions called stone nuts, and in the case of both post and tower mills the drive to the stones may be from above (overdrift) or below (underdrift). The early great spur wheels were wooden, of compass arm construction, with two or three arms mortised through the wooden upright shaft in the same way as the early brake wheels; a few survive and fine examples can be seen in the smock mills at Lacey Green, Bucks, and Hildenborough, Kent. Later, wheels were of clasp arm construction or with iron hubs and arms and wood rims, or occasionally with iron hubs and rims and wood arms, as at New Bolingbroke Mill, Lincolnshire. The latest of all were of all iron construction, sometimes cast solid, sometimes cast in halves bolted together and frequently with wooden cogs. In the north-west the iron spur teeth were often extended above or below the wheel rim, bevelled inwards, and drove auxiliary machinery and the sack hoist through a bevel pinion on a countershaft. The size of wheels varied from five feet diameter or over in the case of some post mills, to the thirteen foot diameter wheel in Old Buckenham Mill, Norfolk, driving five pairs of stones and a flour-dressing machine. In a few mills two great spur wheels and upright shafts were used, driving two sets of stones on different floors, either of which could be driven by wind or an auxiliary engine, Pilling tower mill in the Lancashire Fylde being a case in point.

The early nuts driven by the great spur wheels were lantern pinions with wooden staves instead of cogs fixed in between two wood flanges; most of them have disappeared in favour of spur-geared nuts, but I came across one in Gayton tower mill in Wirral. The early stone nuts with cogs instead of staves looked not unlike large cart-wheel hubs, being of wood and solid, and in the case of stone nuts in post mills driven direct from the brake or tail wheels, they were all slightly bevelled. Later, nuts were of iron with wooden cogs mortised in and later still they were wholly of iron. The drive from the great spur wheel to the nut was of course originally wood cogs to wood cogs, iron to wood or wood to iron was used and finally, in some cases, iron to iron; but as this last tends to give a noisy drive and one not easy to mesh correctly it was usually avoided.

When stones are driven from above (overdrift) the stone nuts are mounted on quants, as at Saxtead Green, Cranbrook and Sibsey Mills; if, however, the drive is from below (underdrift) the stone nut is mounted on the stone spindle, on top of which the runner stone is balanced. In all cases provision must be made to throw the stone nut out of gear and in the case of a quant this is comparatively easy. Usually a glut box is provided to house the top bearing of the quant; this enables half the bearing to be moved to one side and the quant to be slipped out of it and swung away from the great spur wheel, thus throwing the stone nut out of gear. The quant is unable to swing far on account of the crotch, or forked lower end, which is engaged by a drive that will be described later.

In the case of an underdrift stone with a wooden stone nut, some of the cogs are made easily removable by withdrawing their fixing pins and are known as slip cogs. An iron nut may be mounted on a taper, or on splines on the stone spindle, and be raised and held out of gear by a screw, a rack and pinion, a pivoted forked lever or by two chains which can be wound up on a spindle, this last device being called a rigger. In a few instances a segment of four or five teeth was dovetailed into the rim and could be removed at will, and this was the method employed in Sprowston post mill, Norwich.

XV. STONES, BELL ALARMS AND TENTERING

THE main types of natural stones taken in order of hardness were:

French or *burr:* a freshwater quartz.
Cullin or *blue:* a German lava.
Peak or *grey:* a millstone grit.

The french stones were used mainly for flour; the cullin stones, though originally for general use, were latterly used chiefly in the north for barley and oats, while the peak stones were used for feed. Naturally many other stones were quarried, in Anglesey, Lancashire, Bucks and elsewhere, but it is doubtful whether any can still be found in use in windmills. The french stones are quarried at La Ferté sous Jouarre, in the Paris basin, and are as a rule built up in two concentric rings (Fig. 49), from sections which look like keystones of an arch.

They are cemented together, have iron bands shrunk on round them to keep them from bursting when running, and they are smoothed over at the back with plaster of paris. Frequently an iron ring was let into the plaster round the eye of the runner stone bearing the maker's name and occasionally the date of manufacture, and some exist today which are more than one hundred years old. The peak stones are quarried in one piece from the living rock at Hathersage near

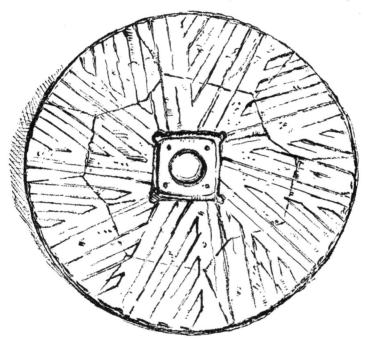

FIG. 49. FRENCH STONE, UNION MILL, CRANBROOK

Sheffield and elsewhere; they are sometimes banded and sometimes not. They are of relatively soft stone, which may last for ten or twelve years in continuous use, and are not used for wheat like french stones. At one time a number of cullin stones were imported; these are blue-black and are quarried at Neider Mending and shipped down the Rhine from Cologne, from which they derive their name. They were evidently very highly thought of in days gone by, for I found one used as a doorstep at Drinkstone post mill in Suffolk. It had been dressed for grinding on both sides, flat on one side and convex on the other, and had been used until it had worn extremely thin at the edge. Grey stones quarried at Whittle in Lancashire were to be found in mills in the Fylde, and Welsh granite stones were used in some of the Anglesey mills. Sizes varied from three feet six inches to five feet diameter, but four-foot stones geared to run normally at about 125 r.p.m. were the most common. The formula used by the old millwrights was as follows:

'To determine the speed of millstones divide the number of inches of the diameter of the stones into 5,000 for grinding flour and 6,000

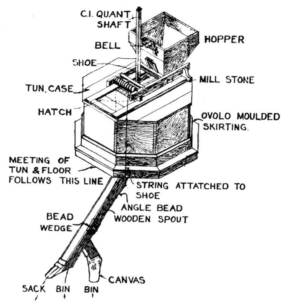

FIG. 50. ISOMETRIC DRAWING OF STONES

for wheat meal and grists; e.g. diameter of stones 48 in. This divided into 6,000 = 125 r.p.m.'

Some runner stones were fitted with Clark & Dunham's patent balances. These consisted of cylindrical metal pockets sunk into the stone on opposite sides near the rim and carrying lead discs on a screw. The mass of these discs could be altered and they could be screwed up and down to balance the stone on both its vertical and its horizontal axes.

Grain is usually stored on the bin floor above the stone floor and is fed by gravity through a grain spout to the hoppers, supported on a rectangular wooden frame or horse which rests on top of the round or octagonal stone casing called a vat or tun (Fig. 50). From the hopper the grain enters the shoe, an inclined tapering trough, hung free at the top from the horse and held by a leaf spring, often of wood, against a square on the quant in the case of overdrift stones. When underdrift stones are used the shoe is held against a three- or four-armed iron spindle called a damsel, which projects above the

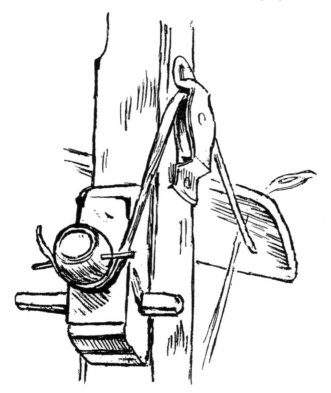

FIG. 51. TWIST PEG, CRANBROOK

runner stone, rotates with it and gets its name from the fact that it makes more noise than anything else in the mill. As the quant or damsel revolves it taps against a block of hard wood in the shoe called the rap, and shakes the grain down the incline. The amount of grain passing can be regulated from the meal floor below by a cord passing down to a twist peg (Fig. 51) located near the meal spout, by means of which the height of the lower end of the shoe can be adjusted. There is often a small adjustable gate in the shoe, either sliding up and down and adjusted by a cord, or like the butterfly valve of a carburettor but on a vertical pivot, and this gate is additional to the twist peg control, while a sliding gate in the shoe or hopper was also used. From the shoe the grain falls into the eye of the runner stone (sometimes lined with metal), passes between the stones, is ground and emerges as meal at the outer edge. Trapped by the vat it is swept round by a tag fixed to the runner and falls down through a hole and via the meal spout into the bin or sack below. In some cases hopper and horse are dispensed with and a very large

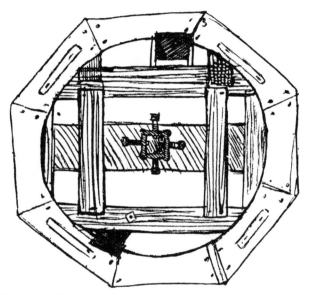

FIG. 52. FRAMING OF A BEDSTONE, HARTEST MILL, SUFFOLK

shoe supported by the wall of the mill is fed with grain direct from the bin above. This was common in the north-west and was found elsewhere, as at Syleham post mill, Suffolk.

When the meal is fed direct into sacks from the meal spout, some form of sack holder or sack jigger is used. This may consist of a wooden bar like a coat hanger with a spike at each end to hold the sack open and a cord to suspend the hanger from a nearby hook; or it may take the form of a round disc of wood with hooks on the outer edge on which the sack is hung with a large hole cut in it eccentrically, through which the meal flows; and frequently the sack jigger is hung with a cord from a forked lever, suspended in its turn from a

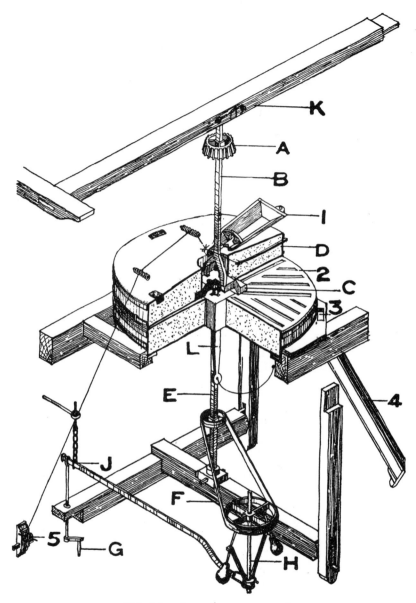

FIG. 53. STONES (IN POST MILL)

A, Stone nut. B, Quant. C, Mace. D, Runner stone. E, Stone spindle. F, Bridge tree. G, Adjusting screw. H, Governors. J, Steelyard. K, Sprattle. L, Grease wedge.

1, Shoe. 2, Bedstone. 3, Meal hole. 4, Meal spout. 5, Control for shoe.

hook and used to shake the contents of the sack by bumping it on the floor. When the sack is full, the neck is tied up and the sack is moved to one side often with a wooden sack truck; I know of one still in use which is nearly one hundred years old and there may be many equally old but undated.

Platform scales were commonly used for weighing up, mostly modern, but a few old ones like those at Sibsey Mill survived. Earlier, beam scales were in use, and a solitary steelyard with a wooden beam still exists in the Cat and Fiddle post mill at Dale Abbey, Derbyshire.

The stationary lower or bedstone of a pair of stones is supported on a timber frame (Fig. 52) usually set in the stone floor itself, or occasionally on a framework or hurst standing on the floor as at Dale Abbey post mill and Dalham smock mill, Suffolk. The stone is packed up off the frame and is surrounded with a round or octagonal plinth or curb which locates the vat surrounding the stones. The iron stone spindle, on which the runner stone is carried (Fig. 53), protrudes upwards through the bedstone and is supported at its lower end by the bridge tree, which carries a bridging box and thrust bearing already referred to in connection with upright shafts. The neck of the stone spindle runs in a bearing let into the bedstone consisting of a cast-iron box with horns at the corners (Fig. 54), wedged into place, which carries three brass bearing pads and one wooden pad with a stem protruding downwards below the stone; this is called the grease wedge and can be removed for the insertion of grease into the bearing. An iron hackle plate holds a close-fitting leather washer on to the top of the cast-iron box to prevent grit and dirt entering the bearing. The top or cock head of the stone spindle is rounded with a tapered square below it, and this sockets into a cast-iron mace which has a slightly hump-backed groove on its top face (Fig. 55). A bow-shaped iron bar is fixed across the eye of the runner stone, the ends being let into it and held with molten lead, sulphur, alum or wooden wedges. This bar is an easy fit in the groove in the top of the mace from which it takes the drive, the weight of the runner stone being carried by the cock head of the stone spindle. The earlier method was to set an iron cross or rynd on the tapered part of the spindle, its four arms being let into the runner stone, and this continued in use in the Anglesey windmills if not elsewhere. The mace assembly was an improvement for it allowed the runner stone to take up a balanced position whereas the rynd was stiff. In the case of overdrift stones the quant is carried and drives by two grooves in the side of the mace, and the stone spindle does not have to transmit the drive as well as supporting the runner stone.

A detailed description of the dressing of millstones by Mr. John Russell is to be found in Appendix D.

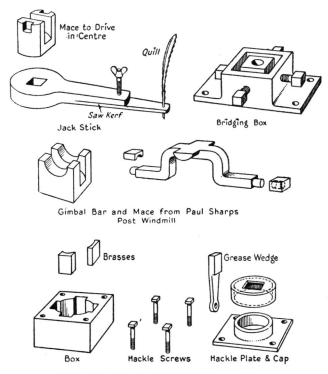

FIGS. 54 AND 55. MILL STONE DETAILS

So that the miller may be warned when grain is running low in the hopper a bell alarm was used. These alarms were found almost universally in England and their necessity arose from the fact that should the stones run short of grain they might touch; in so doing there was a risk both of fire from sparks and of the stones being blunted and needing redressing. The simplest type of alarm as seen at Friskney Tofts post mill, Lincolnshire, was a bell attached to an ordinary bell spring in the hopper with a string attached to the shoe; normally the bell was buried in the grain and when uncovered the vibrating shoe rang the bell. The most usual method, however, was to fix one end of a piece of leather to the inside of the hopper near the bottom, attaching a string to the other end and passing the string out through the opposite side of the hopper. The string was connected to a bell in various ways and while the grain in the hopper weighed down the leather the string remained taut; as soon as the grain fell low, however, the leather, relieved of its weight, rose, overcome by the weight of the bell, which fell against some moving part and was rung. Many and ingenious were the arrangements of strings, pulleys, levers, strikers and pivots which were combined to form this most Heath Robinson affair; but all worked, being rung against shafts, wheels, pins or even the top of the runner stone, while in some cases bells of different notes were used to tell the miller which hopper needed refilling. But in derelict mills bells do not long survive, being the first souvenir to be stolen by intruders. (Fig. 56.)

The object of the miller is to grind his grain to a consistent degree of fineness, and this depends on three main factors:

Firstly, the speed of the stones as determined by the speed of the sails.

Secondly, the feed of grain to the stones as regulated by the shoe and gate.

Thirdly, the gap between the faces of the stones.

The regulation of this last factor is called tentering and consists of raising and lowering the runner stone in relation to the bedstone. The footstep or thrust bearing of the stone spindle rests on a horizontal bridge tree of wood or iron. Some iron bridge trees are fixed and the footstep bearing itself is raised and lowered independently of it, but the bridge tree is usually pivoted at one end and is raised and lowered slightly by means of two levers called the bray and steelyard respectively, thus permitting a heavy running stone to be manipulated easily by hand. In this connection must be borne in mind the extremely fine adjustment in the region of hundredths of an inch which is required. Independent hand adjustment is provided by the lighter screw, which passes through the free end of the bridge tree, and moves it so that the stones may be set to a minimum distance apart as required, but final control is by the steelyard. Originally this lever was operated by hand, usually by means of a cord, but the replacement of hand tentering by automatic governors filled a very long-felt want of windmillers. That James Watt invented the governor is a fallacy—he only patented its application to steam engines. Captain Stephen Hooper has been claimed as the inventor, but there is only one published statement to this effect and no confirmation as far as I am aware. But Thomas Mead was granted a patent in 1787 [1] for a 'Regulator for Wind and other Mills', which shows centrifugal governors applied to furling sail cloths, lag-type governors applied to tentering stones, and also claims to apply them to flour-dressing machines. One of the few complete surviving hand-tentering gears can still be seen at High Salvington post mill, Sussex, with a governor in addition to control the same pair of stones.

FIG. 56. GOVERNORS AND BELL ALARM, UNION MILL, CRANBROOK

Governors in windmills were most usually belt-driven, sometimes from the upright shaft, sometimes from the stone spindle, though in Lincolnshire they were often gear-driven from the base of the upright shaft. At Pakenham tower mill, Suffolk, they are chain-driven from the stone spindles, and in quite a number of instances all over the country they are mounted on the stone spindles themselves. Very often in Lincolnshire one pair of governors controlled from two to four pairs of stones, but independent control seems to have been more generally favoured. Governors varied greatly in design and included the centrifugal, pendulum and lag types; the oldest examples were largely hand-forged with lead weights travelling outwards on curved horns, and in Kent a few had links and arms of wood instead of iron.

[1] Specification, No. 1628.

In the north tentering without compensating for the speed of the mill was the rule when husking barley or oats, the gap between the stones being pre-set and left at from a quarter inch to five-sixteenth inch and the stiff rynd was used in the runner stone.

XVI. SACK HOISTS, MACHINES AND INDUSTRIAL USES

Brush me well and keep me clean,
The work I do will soon be seen,
But I am like the ladies fair,
I love to dress I do declare.
> (Lines on the bolter casing in
> Coddington tower mill, Notts.)

In order to raise the grain for grinding to the required floor so that it could feed down to the stones by gravity, a mechanical device known as a sack hoist was generally used. The date of its introduction is unknown, but in its most primitive form it consisted of a rope passing over a pulley fixed to a beam projecting from the rear gable of a post mill. This seems to be indicated in the Walsoken Brass at King's Lynn, Norfolk, dated 1346, and is clearly shown in the fifteenth-century window in Greenford Church, Middlesex.

The next development was to pass an endless hand rope over a large wooden rope pulley, on the axle of which was a long drum of much smaller diameter. When the hand rope was pulled the sack chain was wound up on the drum; even so a considerable effort was required to raise a sack containing a combe of two hundred and eighty pounds of grain, although most millers can carry such a sack on the level with an ease astonishing to the tyro, and in the old tide mill at Stambridge, Essex, where one of these hoists survived, it was sarcastically referred to as the 'mandraulic' by those who had to operate it.

The earliest reference to a sack hoist has already been quoted, and the power-driven hoist consists in its essentials of a sack chain with a ring at the end for making a running noose round the sack neck. The chain hangs down through all the floors in the mill passing through double-flap hinged traps in the floor, which open upwards automatically as it rises and fall closed behind it, while they have to

138

be held open if a sack is to be lowered. A cord which runs down through each floor to the bottom floor is pulled and held to operate the hoist; it is usually worked by hand, but sometimes a stirrup is fixed at the end for foot working on the bottom floor. In some Lincolnshire tower mills an endless sack chain hanging down from a driven chain wheel was used and the sack was hooked to the chain. The late Mr. W. B. Horton of Hythe, born in 1839, saw a sack hoist chain made of wood preserved as a curiosity by his father, who had it out of Black (post) Mill, which he had pulled down.

While there are many variations the principle of operation of most of these hoists is a slipping belt. A slack belt is taken upwards from a driven shaft to a belt pulley mounted on one end of the sack-chain drum. The bearing at this end is mounted on a movable wooden solepiece controlled by a lever to which the operating cord is attached. When the cord is pulled it raises the solepiece, which in turn raises the chain drum and tightens the belt and the drive is maintained as long as the cord is held. Sometimes a chain was used instead of a belt and sometimes a jockey pulley was used to tighten the belt, while at Jolesfield in Sussex, there were two such pulleys; the jockey pulley method causes a reversal of stress, however, which is bad for the belt. Most of the chain drums were horizontal, but at Kenninghall, in Norfolk, a vertical drum was used, and like some horizontal drums had a counter-weight to pull off the drive.

The most common variant of the slack-belt drive is a friction wheel acting on a friction surface below the wallower in the case of a tower mill (Fig. 57), and on the outer rim of the tail wheel in the case of a post mill; while at Shelford post mill in Nottinghamshire, the inner rim of the brake wheel was used as a friction surface. At Bodle Street Green post mill in Sussex the drive was by spur wheel from the shanks of the cogs projecting behind the brake wheel, while at Argos Hill post mill, also in Sussex, and in some other post mills the inner side of the face of the brake wheel cogs was used, and at Sprowston post mill, Norwich, the drive was by means of a cone clutch driven from the brake wheel. The drive for ordinary slack-belt sack hoists is usually taken from a pulley on the windshaft in the case of post mills and from the upright shaft by gearing and a countershaft in the case of tower mills. This latter drive may take the form of a bevel wheel on the upright shaft, a geared bevel ring fixed to the top or bottom of the great spur wheel, or in the north-west, as before mentioned, a bevel extension of the teeth of the great spur wheel; the wheels are as a rule constantly in mesh, and very often other machines were driven from the countershaft. To load full sacks from the mill on to wagons, hinged sack slides were sometimes used down one side of the ladders of post mills, the sacks being let down them with a chain or rope, and a neat sack loader at Upminster smock mill, Essex, was contrived by lowering a hinged portion of the stage when required.

The machinery of a mill is by no means confined to the stones; sifters, dressing machines and others of various kinds and degrees of

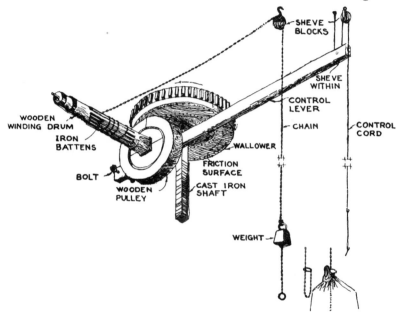

FIG. 57. ISOMETRIC VIEW OF A SACK TACKLE

efficiency were used but the most important of all were the bolters and the wire machines, which were used for dressing flour from the bran and middlings and were in common if declining use in England, right up to 1916.

The bolter was greatly improved by Messrs. Blackmore of Wandsworth in 1783. It consisted of a wooden casing about six feet long in which was placed a rotatable inclined wooden reel about twenty-three inches diameter. This was covered with a loosely fitting, removable, seamless woollen bolting cloth, leather-bound and laced up at each end with cords running through the leather like a pyjama cord; the reel was open at the lower end and closed at the upper end by a coarse-mesh conical net. Six inclined wooden bars fixed to the casing were spaced round the reel, leaving it about a half-inch of clearance. Meal was fed into the reel via an overhead hopper at the upper end and through the net which caught any large foreign matter such as straws or even mice! As the reel revolved the meal caused the cloth to sag and strike against the fixed bars, the flour was knocked through the cloth, whilst the bran and middlings tailed out at the

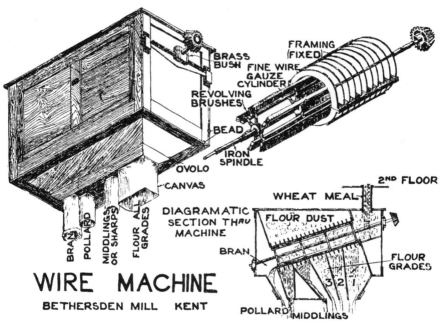

FIG. 58. ISOMETRIC VIEW OF A WIRE MACHINE

lower end. The bolting cloth made of wool was very liable to attack by moth. In Krunitz *Encyclopaedia* of 1810 it is stated 'a great deal of bolting cloth comes from England and although the yard costs twice as much as the German it lasts much longer'. Originally bolting was done not by the miller but by hand by a bolter or meal man, or by the baker using a sieve or teme.[1]

A dressing machine, known as a wire machine (Fig. 58), invented by a Mr. Atown of Norfolk was very commonly used for dressing

[1] By his ardent and untiring exertions 'setting the temes on fire'. Bennett and Elton, Vol. III, p. 172.

flour. It is illustrated by Telford in 1786 [1] and is similar to the bolter, but in place of the rotary reel, a fixed wooden framed drum was used made in halves, often of mahogany, and covered inside in sections with wire mesh of progressively fine gauges. A rotary spindle passing down the centre carried brushes which brushed the flour through the wire and allowed the bran to tail out at the end. A similar machine used for cleaning wheat had a tapered cylinder, the spindle being horizontal. The ribs were fewer in number than the wire machine and much stronger; the brushes were, of course, tapered to suit, and the spindle could be adjusted endways to brush as hard as might be necessary. What cleaning was done was of little account, no fan drew away the dust, most of which found its way into the wheat. The position of all these machines in post mills was varied, but as a general rule they were placed in the tail of the mill, either across it or on either side. The feed to bolters and wire machines was by a shoe as with stones, the rap being struck twice per revolution of the spindle. Occasionally small governors were fitted operating a gate to regulate the feed, but more often the rate of feed was controlled as for stones with light cords and feed pegs; these regulated the height of the shoe, knocked by the double cam or beater on a spindle, and a sliding gate placed vertically at the front of the hopper. Sometimes the speed was also regulated by a jockey pulley, controlled by a weighted cord, which allowed the driving belt to slip when the speed increased unduly.

I have come across two machines in one casing in Anglesey and both there and in the north-west of England, groat machines, which in the past were used for preparing oats for porridge, were also found. To prepare them for grinding, the oats were first roasted in a kiln adjoining the mill; they were then passed through a pair of stones set at a constant distance apart, this being the length of the average oat, and the husk was split off the grain. From the stones they passed to an inclined wire reel in the top of the groat machine and here the dust, formed when the oats were roasted, was brushed out. As the oats and husks tailed out of the cylinder they, together with the dust, were exposed to a draught of air from a wooden fan. The husks and dust, being light, were blown into the chamber beyond the machine known as the husk-cupboard; while the groats, as

---

[1] 'On Mills', manuscript by Thomas Telford, edited by E. L. Burne, *Transactions of the Newcomen Society*.

they were now termed, fell down into two spouts, the lighter and poorer groats being carried to the spout furthest from the fan. This fan had four wooden blades, built up swastika fashion round the fan spindle, and was about four feet diameter by eighteen inches wide. It was driven by a belt, and was regulated by belt slip, either by means of a jockey pulley, or by moving the spindle backwards and forwards in a slotted bearing. The oats were shelled with a quarter inch to five-sixteenth inch gap between the stones and a fixed rynd in the stones was used, the oats being put through twice, lowering the stone for the second shelling because the oats were not graded. After grinding, the sifter or jumper described below was used; the top sieve took the shudes, or unshelled oats, the middle took the coarse ground stuff; a fan blew out the shudes from the middle sieve, and these were known as meal shudes and used for feed; what came from the third sieve was bagged up and the remainder went through the stones again.

The sifter called a jumper or jog-scry was less frequently met with than other machines; it consisted of several inclined rectangular wire sieves of different meshes each slightly overlapping the one below it, coupled together and given a jolting motion in order to feed down and grade the meal or groats fed in at the upper end. At Friston post mill, Suffolk, which still contains one of these jog-scrys, there is also an inclined covered sieve under the bin spout feeding the hopper of one pair of stones together with a funnel in the hopper. When the funnel empties it rises and opens a trap at the top of the sieve; the grain runs down, is sieved and flows into the funnel, which falls, shuts the trap and is again gradually emptied as it feeds the stones. This contrivance is known as the balance dish. In addition to all these there were smutters, which removed smut from wheat and looked like a short stumpy wire machine set vertically, modern oat crushers, bean kibblers, centrifugal flour-dressers, and grind-stones for sharpening mill bills.

The drives for all these machines also varied; in post mills the initial drive was most commonly from the face of the brake wheel or tail wheel cogs by a skew-geared pinion, and sometimes by an ordinary spur pinion from the sides of the cogs, while occasionally a friction drive from the rim of the tail wheel was used. Sometimes an inner row of teeth was put on the brake wheel or an internal gear on the tail wheel and used for this purpose, but the most curious drive was to be seen in the derelict post mill at Hykeham Moor in

Lincolnshire, where by a system of face gears and right-angle drives the power was taken from the brake wheel via a heavy wooden shaft outside the main frame of the mill body, and down to a machine in the tail of the mill. The weatherboarding of the roof had been extended outwards to cover this drive and the effect from outside was as if part of the roof was slipping off. This drive was not unique; a similar method was employed in the post mill in Lincoln which was taken down in 1919, and also elsewhere. In tower mills the drive was usually taken from the upright shaft to a countershaft, most commonly by bevel drive either from an independent wheel or from a bevel ring fixed to the arms of the great spur wheel; alternatively the drive was by a spur pinion similar to a stone nut and driven by the great spur wheel. In the north-west, as has already been mentioned, the iron cogs of the great spur wheel were often extended as bevels beyond the rim to drive the machines, and in most cases the final drive, both in post and tower mills, was by belt.

Records of windmills in England used for purposes other than grinding grain or raising water are not numerous, and other trades seem to have been served mainly by water power; a few mills, however, were built for sawing wood. The first is said to have been introduced by a Dutchman in 1633, forty-one years after the first wind sawmill was set to work in the Netherlands. The last to be used in England solely for that purpose was a smock mill at Punnett's Town, Sussex, which supplied power to a sawmill and joinery works. It had been moved from Rye, Sussex, in 1862, and was dismantled in 1929. One of the two tower mills standing in the same yard at Cawston, Norfolk, was used for sawing wood for making herring boxes; there were once three sawmills in Norwich, and the ten-sided smock grist mill at Wangford, Suffolk, started life as a sawmill on Lord Stradbroke's estate, while a sawmill stood on the south bank of the Thames where now is Hungerford Bridge.

A large five-sailed tower mill at Hessle, Yorkshire (Plate XIII), and a very small tower mill at Linton, Cambridgeshire, both ground chalk for the production of whiting; the octagonal stone-built tower grist mill at Littleworth Common, Oxfordshire, was once owned by the Liberator Company and like Melin Baent, in Anglesey, in other hands, was used by them for grinding ochre quarried near by. Berney Arms drainage mill, Norfolk (Fig. 43), was at one time additionally used for grinding cement clinker produced from the natural mixture of chalk and clay dredged from the river beds near by, while at Islington, London (Plate XXXII), white lead was ground with mill stones in two windmills and the base of one of these mills now houses an electric motor to do the same work.

In Norwich bark-grinding was done by wind, and at Carson Hill in the same city one of the towers of the old city walls is called the snuff tower, since it was once surmounted by a windmill grinding this commodity. Two tower mills ground snuff in Bristol and two snuffmills were built by a Mr. Leach on a hillock in the grounds of Devizes Castle, Wiltshire (Plate XXIX). They eventually passed into the hands of Mr. Benjamin Anstie, who drove about in a yellow and black horse-drawn carriage on the doors of which were painted:

'Who'd a' thought it?
Noses bought it'.

And there is the 'Who'd a' thought it' Inn at Fyfield not far away to this day.

Pressing oil from linseed was another use to which the wind was harnessed and wind-driven oil mills were used at King's Lynn, Norfolk, Gainsborough, Lincolnshire, and on Cathedral Mount, Liverpool, within the last century. The operation, as I have seen it in France and the Netherlands, was as follows: the linseed was first crushed in a modern crusher; it was then heated on a flat-topped stove being stirred all the while by two-bladed stirrers. After this it was placed in horse-hair sacks between iron plates and the oil was pressed out by pressing stamps and wedges. The resulting cake was removed from the sacks, crushed by other iron-shod stamps, heated, stirred and repressed, the process being repeated three times in all and the oil from each pressing kept separate. The hollow post mill at Southwark ground bones and later flint for china, Brazil Mill, a wind and water mill at Wandsworth, drove a logwood mill for dye, and there was also a drug mill at Lambeth. Finally in Smeaton's Designs, preserved in the library of the Royal Society, are drawings which include designs of all or some portion of the following:

Wakefield, Yorkshire.	Oil and logwood rasping mill.
Barking, Essex.	Logwood mill.
Nine Elms, Vauxhall, London.	Flint mill for china.
Leeds, Yorkshire.	ditto
Chimney Mill, Newcastle-on-Tyne.	Corn- and snuffmill.

PART THREE

The Men

PART THREE

The Men

★

XVII. ORIGINS AND CUSTOMS

VERY little work has been done on the origin of the windmill in England since the publication of Bennett and Elton's *History of Corn Milling*.[1] On the purely historical side it contains more information than has been collected since, and while many subsequent writers have benefited from it few have acknowledged the fact.

All the known references to windmills of the twelfth century and earlier are considered in detail and most are shown to be false, notably a monkish forgery of the time of Henry II alleging the grant of a windmill to the Abbey of Croyland in 833. The first acceptable reference to a windmill is found to be that contained in the *Chronicles of Joycelyn de Brakelond*, concerning a windmill built in 1191 by Dean Herbert on his glebe lands at Bury St. Edmunds. This infringed the manorial rights of the Abbey and Dean Herbert was forced to demolish his windmill. This is not very much later than the earliest authenticated reference to a windmill in Western Europe in a deed *c.* 1180 which gives a piece of land near a windmill to the Abbey of St. Sauvère de Vicomte in Normandy.[2] While all earlier references have so far proved false, there is always the hope that some new and fully authenticated ones may be discovered.

Later research has shown that the earliest known illustration of a windmill is contained in the English *Windmill Psalter, c.* 1270, probably written at Canterbury, bought by William Morris in 1896, and

[1] 4 vols., 1898–1904. [2] *Jour. Brit. Arch. Assoc.*, Vol. VI, p. 403.

now in the Pierpont Morgan Library in New York. This and suc-
ceeding manuscripts all show post mills; the earliest known illustrations of tower mills are in a French illuminated manuscript made
in 1420 for the Porter family in England and now also in the Pierpont Morgan Library; they show a type that has persisted in north-
west France to the present day. The mechanism of the early post mill
is like that of an early water mill turned upside-down, the water-mill
drive being from below upwards and the windmill drive from above
downwards; and it is my opinion, in spite of absence of proof, that
the origin of the windmill considered from the mechanical standpoint

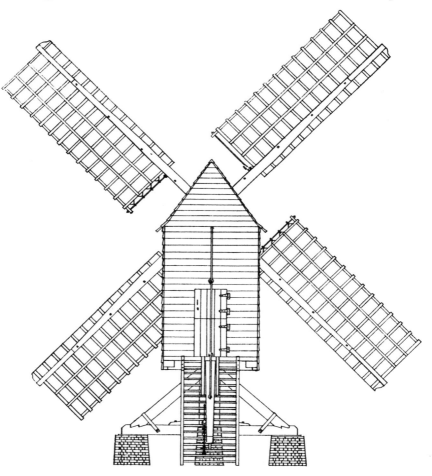

is just that and no more. I have seen, though I do not possess, a photograph of a post mill in Russia, with the windshaft in the lower part of the mill body; the drive could only have been upwards, as in a water mill, and the connection of ideas is obvious. In England the oldest post mill still standing is that at Bourn, Cambridgeshire, known to have been in existence in 1636 (Figs. 59 and 60); the working parts have been replaced from time to time but the structure is the original one.

The only remains of the oldest tower mill are two floors of the fifteenth-century stone tower, wrongly called the beacon, at Burton

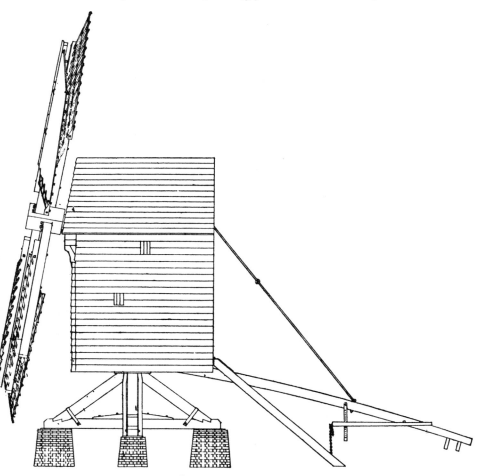

FIGS. 59 AND 60. BOURN MILL, CAMBRIDGESHIRE

Dasset, Warwickshire. It is only fair to add that Bennett and Elton were not aware of these early illustrations or the age of these mills.

At Bury St. Edmunds it was the Milling Soke that was broken by the Dean, and these Soke rights gave the Lord of the Manor the monopoly of corn-grinding mills. Bennett and Elton go very fully into feudal laws and customs and from them I quote passages which summarise the situation and which they themselves quote from original sources.

'Soke had not its origin by statute law, but by the individual action of manorial lords on their own estates. Such a lord built a mill for the common behoof of the residents in his manor, hence, on the one hand he refused to allow anyone to build on his land a competing mill and on the other compelled his tenants to give the mill their custom. The practice thus originally existed only in certain isolated manors. The lord of the manor could move, increase or decrease the number of mills, always provided that the capacity met the requirements of the residents in the Soke district. When alternative mills existed and one was pulled down, the custom of Soke was broken by the deprivation of the option. Some manors were entirely exempt from soke, either by the lords never claiming it or by their granting it away and freeing the residents.'

'Milling soke never came into existence by Act of Parliament, was never legally abolished by law; and finally it was either broken by tenants or purchased by them, if indeed owners, in view of the frequent trouble of enforcing it, did not voluntarily abandon it.'

They quote the manorial custom that not only were the tenants of the manor bound to grind at the lord's mill at a fixed rate of toll (a proportion of the grist ground), but that the lord's corn should be ground free and given complete priority over that of the tenants. If, however, the mill was allowed to get into disrepair, the tenants could have their corn ground elsewhere. Minor repairs were usually the responsibility of the tenant miller, major repairs of the lord.

The ordinary rate of toll for grinding was one-sixteenth for corn grown on the estate. Bought corn, if it were dried at the lord's kiln, must also be ground there, the toll again being one-sixteenth. Bought corn, if not dried by the lord's fuel, must be ground at the mill also, the toll, however, being only one-twenty-fourth.

The substitution of money payment for toll in kind was not generally introduced till the thirteenth century. It was not introduced by

xviib. Penny Hill six-sailed tower mill, Lincolnshire, showing a windshaft with a cross, now derelict.

xviia. Downfield Mill, Soham, Cambridgeshire, showing a windshaft with a poll end, still at work.

XVIII. Argos Hill Mill, Sussex, by Thomas Hennell.

XIX. Halnaker Mill, Sussex, by William Turner of Oxford.

xx. Eld's Mill, Coventry, Warwickshire, with twin fantails.

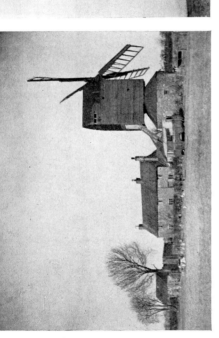

xxib. Brill Mill, Buckinghamshire, built 1668, now a landmark.

xxid. Clifton Mill, Lancashire, now derelict.

xxia. Sproxton Mill, Leicestershire, moved from Castle Bytham, Lincolnshire, and now demolished.

xxic. Holywell Mill, Huntingdonshire, dated 1741, now demolished.

xxiia. Gibraltar Mill, Great Bardfield, Essex, now derelict.

xxiib. Syleham Mill, Suffolk, still at
work.

xxiic. Ashton Mill, Somerset, now
derelict.

xxiid. Bembridge Mill, Isle of Wight,
once preserved, now derelict.

xxiii*a*. Eye Mill, Peterborough, now derelict.

xxiii*b*. Little Hadham Mill, Herts, now derelict.

xxiii*c*. Stokenchurch Mill, Oxfordshire, with three crosstrees and six quarterbars, built 1736, collapsed 1926.

xxiii*d*. Stevington Mill, Bedfordshire, dated 1783 and now preserved.

xxiv*a*. Heapham Mill, Lincolnshire, built 1875, still at work.

xxiv*b*. Waltham Mill, Lincolnshire, built 1880, on the site of a post mill. A six-sailed mill still at work with four sails.

xxiv*c*. Burgh-le-Marsh five-sailed mill, Lincolnshire, still at work.

xxiv*d*. Hoyles' five-sailed mill, Alford, Lincolnshire, built 1837 and still at work.

statute but simply by manorial civic law, the two systems enduring till 1st July, 1796, when at last a statute came into operation rendering toll in money compulsory. It included the clause: 'Every miller shall put up in his mill a table of prices for grinding or the amount of toll required at his mill, under a penalty not exceeding 20s. All penalties to go half to the informer and the other half to the poor.'

A few of these old notices survived and I reproduce here some that I have come across. The first in Darsham post mill, Suffolk, built in 1801 and now demolished, was on the flour-dresser and read:

Notice is hereby given
That from the 6th day of July 1809
Whoever has any corn ground at this
Mill, shall pay the price of 2s per Comb
for grinding, and 1s per Comb for
dressing Wheat; 1s 6d per Comb for
grinding Hog Corn & the accustomed
allowance for waste in grinding and
dressing the same—The above prices
to be paid if demanded before the Corn
is taken out of the Mill, otherwise
a part thereof shall then and there be
left equivalent to the amount of the
Charge of grinding and the quantity
so left shall be ascertained by the then
current price of Corn of the like description & quality.

A notice on the flour dresser in Hoyles five-sailed tower mill at Alford, Lincolnshire, reads:

LIST OF
CHARGES
FOR
GRINDING

WHEAT GROUND AND DRESSED	9d PER STRIKE.
DITTO FOR TOLL	8 LBS PER STRIKE.
DITTO FOR TOLL	30 LBS FOR 4 STRIKE.
BARLEY, BEANS, OATS &C	4½d PER STRIKE.
DITTO FOR TOLL	7 LBS PER STRIKE.

August 23, 1872.

The Men

In Downfield Mill, Soham, Cambridgeshire, on a beam on the first floor is a printed flysheet which reads:

List of prices
agreed to by
The Soham Millers
Grinding and Dressing Corn.

	s. d.
Wheat Ground only	2. – per comb.
Ditto if ground and dressed.	3. 6. ditto.
Barley, bullock and hog corn of any description.	1. 6. ditto.

WALTER MANNING.

THOS. PEAK.

LUKE STAPLES.

WILLIAM BULLMAN.

WM. MARKHAM.

HENRY STAPLES.

Soham. Oct. 1854.

In Melin y Bont, Bryn-dû, Anglesey, was a fine, black-painted, undated toll-board with the charges for grinding in white lettering. It was of course in Welsh and in translation read as follows:

AMOUNT OF TAX THAT WILL BE CHARGED AT MELIN Y BONT BRYN DU
FOR GRINDING A QUARTER OF WHEAT & DRESSING   6 QUARTS.
FOR GRINDING A QUARTER OF BARLEY AND DRESSING   6 QUARTS.
FOR GRINDING A QUARTER OF BARLEY OR OATS FOR PIGS.   6 QUARTS.
FOR ONE QUARTER OF OATS TO THE KILN AND DRESSING INTO OATMEAL
ONE BUSHEL EITHER IN GROATS OR FLOUR.

In Kingsland Mill, Holyhead, Anglesey, on either side of the main door were two toll cupboards or kests; these were used for the reception of toll and a share out at the end of the week was made between the last owner to work the mill and her sons.

Some windmills were built on land which survived as common land after enclosure. The post mill on Rougham Common, Suffolk, which had a thatched roundhouse, was a Glebe Mill, while at Brill, Bucks (Plate XXI), there were two post mills on the common; one was undermined by quarrying operations, while the other has been preserved and is now in the care of the Bucks County Council.

There were mills owned by clubs or societies and run for mutual benefit; such was the Hucknall post mill, Nottingham, owned by the Hucknall Mill Sick Club, the Society tower mill, Portsmouth, which had a statue as a finial on its domed cap, and the Subscription Mill in Dansom Lane, Hull. The five-sailed Co-operative Mill at Whitby, Yorkshire, was a very large tower mill, the base of which was eventually incorporated into a garage. Parish mills were also built by well-disposed people inspired by the Society for Bettering the Conditions of the Poor. One such mill, built at Chislehurst, Kent, in 1796, ground for the poor on Mondays. The mill was made and erected by John Hall, the Dartford millwright, and his bill amounted to £1,765, besides £214, the cost of the house, and £44 for the fencing. At Epworth, Lincolnshire, let into a brick wall beside a house is a stone on which is inscribed:

> This mill is the
> equal property of
> subscribers 1805,
> Both rich and poor a
> friend will find
> Who standeth here
> their corn to grind.

The mill in question was demolished in 1921.

XVIII. WINDMILLS IN WAR

THE importance of Anglesey as one-time centre of milling is shown by the fact that no less than thirty-seven mill sites were marked on the ordnance maps of 1923 and most had been corn mills. It was by occupying Anglesey, the granary of North Wales, that the English subdued the Welsh on the mainland; but, as has been pointed out, the North Welsh eventually revenged themselves by roofing England with slates. Mark Antony Lower quotes the following:[1] 'On the day of the battle of Lewes, May 14th 1264, during the flight of the troops of Henry III before the victorious barons, Richard, King of the Romans, the King's younger brother,

[1] *Trans. Sussex Arch. Soc.*, Vol. I, 1832.

took refuge in a windmill, barring the door, and for awhile defending himself from the fury of his pursuers. At length, amidst derisive cries, such as, "Come out, you bad miller! . . . You, forsooth, to turn a wretched mill-master; you, who defied us all so proudly, and would have no meaner title than King of the Romans, and always August!" —he surrendered himself to Sir John Befs, or Bevis, a follower of Gilbert de Clare.[1] The popular ballad composed on this occasion avers that—

> The Kyng of Alemaigne wende do full well
> He saisede the mulne for a castel.
> With hare sharpe swerdes he ground the stel,
> He wende that the sayles were mangonel
>
> The Kyng of Alemaigne gederede ys host
> Makede him a castel of a mulne post.[2]
>
> Percy's *Rel. Ant. Eng. Poet.*

The other historical Sussex windmill is that at Winchelsea, which nearly proved fatal to King Edward the First. The King was at that then important place in the month of August 1297, on his way to Flanders. Thomas of Walsingham describes what might have been a very serious accident as 'the miracle of the King's salvation', in the following terms:

'Whilst the King was dwelling near Winchelsea, he proposed to go one day to the port to take a view of his Fleet, and having entered the town, when he had just ridden over against the bulwarks, and was about to survey the Fleet at the lowest station, it happened that he approached a certain windmill, of which there were several in the town; and his horse being frightened with the noise of the mill, and with the quickly revolving sails, refused to proceed; and as the horse was vigorously urged on by the King by whip and spur, he leaped over the bulwarks; upon which, out of the multitude of horse and foot who followed the King, or had assembled to have a look at him, no one thought but that the King had perished, or had, at least, been stunned by the leap. But Divine Providence so disposing, the horse fell upon his feet, even from such a height, into a road, which

---

[1] *Blaauw's Barons' War*, p. 180.

[2] Wende, imagined; saisede, seized; stel, a post; mangonel, a war-engine to cast stones with; gederede, gathered; ys, his; mulne-post, mill-post.

from recent rains was softened with mud, into which the horse was able to slip for twelve feet, and yet did not fall; and being turned round with another bridle by the King, he ascended directly to the gate, through which he entered unhurt, and the people who were waiting for him were filled with wonder and delight at his miraculous escape.' [1]

Bennett and Elton quote cases in the Civil War in which windmills figure. From Edge Hill post mill, on 23rd October, 1642, Charles I witnessed his first battle and met with his first repulse. On 14th June, 1645, Charles again stood in a windmill and saw at Naseby his last irrevocable defeat. Charles II escaped from the defeat of Worcester in company with Richard Penderell, was chased at midnight by men from Eveleth Mill who believed them to be rogues, and he finally escaped to safety on the back of Humphrey Penderell's mill horse from Whiteladies near Boscobel.

At Chester in July 1643 'to prevent the enemy making lodgement to the annoyance of the City the great windmill without the North Gate was taken down'. At Liverpool an appeal of the Parliamentary Corporation in 1644 to the Cromwellian legislature proved successful and in October 1646 an order of Parliament invested the Borough with the sequestered Molyneux estates in the town. But while in 1644 the Corporation had prayed to be granted 'windmilnes' the order only empowered them to seize 'a wyndmilne'. This was that at Townsend, the only one left on the Molyneux estate in Liverpool; the other, Eastham Mill, had apparently been destroyed during the siege that had closed with the capturing of the town by the Royalists, 2nd June, 1644.

To come three hundred years on in time, the tower mill at Coddington, Nottinghamshire, was damaged by blast from a German land mine, and another at Toynton, Lincolnshire, shielded some houses from bomb blast, which its round brick tower deflected. The tower mill at Coleby Heath, Lincolnshire, was pulled down and another at Oakington, Cambridgeshire, blown up, because of their proximity to airfields, and there were probably other direct casualties of which I am unaware.

[1] Translated in Cooper's *Winchelsea*, pp. 57, 58.

XIX. THE MILLER

Blow wind, blow! and go, mill, go!
That the miller may grind his corn;
And the baker may bake it,
And into bread make it,
And bring us a loaf in the morn.

(Nursery Rhyme, *c.* 1812.)

IN medieval times the miller and his trade were as strictly regulated as they are today, although naturally in different ways, and the miller was not regarded as being inherently honest. That he was not alone in this respect is shown by the old rhyme which runs:

Take a miller who does not steal
And a lawyer who is leal
And a priest who is not greedy,
And set the three a dead corpse by,
And by the virtue of the three
The dead corpse will quickened be.

The old jibe was that an honest miller had a tot or tuft of hair in the palm of each hand, to which the miller's ripost was that only an honest man could see it. It is said that the only miller known to have had such a tot lived at Chalvington, near Lewes, Sussex; finding success in business impossible he hanged himself in his own mill.

The miller was said by Chaucer to have 'a thumb of gold' and millers certainly tended to acquire a broad thumb through constantly feeling and testing meal and flour between thumb and finger in order to judge its fineness by 'rule of thumb'. It is for this reason that the little bull-heads of the streams are called millers' thumbs. I quoted this on one occasion and a lady present showed me her very spatulate thumbs saying that she came of a long line of millers all of whom had had this characteristic. The question as to whether the milling was the cause of the hereditary thumb or vice versa is not likely to be determined.

Another folk tale reflecting on the miller's honesty had a wide circulation; I quote an English version later on, but here it is as I was told it by an old Welsh farmer in very laboured English whilst we were leaning on a gate and looking at the shell of a windmill tower near Pentre-berw in Anglesey.

The Miller

'There was a miller's boy who was a bit simple. Someone question-
ing him and finding him so asked him what he *did* know.

' "Why," he said, "that the miller's pigs are fat." Then, very
quickly, seeing that he had let a secret fall. "But I don't know how
they get so." '

And the old farmer added, 'Was not he a saucy kitten?'

Mr. John Bryant, the Colchester millwright (Plate XXX), once
wrote to me: 'My father at the age of 14 used to drive the millers cart
and at that time he could carry a sack of flour weighing 20 stone. All
my young time flour was weighed at 20 stone. I suppose this genera-
tion has lost some of its stamina. I hope I shall not tire you but I
want to mention a few facts concerning the old trade to show you
how the poor millers of those days groaned about hard times and still
managed to bring up a large family and leave a tidy pile behind
them. First my grandfather worked two mills: the windmill as
long as there was a breeze, then walk 2 miles to the water mill at
Layer and work the water out for the magnificent sum of 14s. per
week; beside that he had to keep all accounts and at the end of the
week, after working sometimes close on a hundred hours a week, he
carried his wages home on his back in the shape of flour for the
family needs. To get enough to carry on with the few necessaries of
life my grandmother kept a small school so as to bring in a few
pence. My father had to start work very young and for a very small
wage; I have heard him say how he sometimes used to smash through
the toll gates if he had not the 3d. for the toll. I was sixteen when a
gentleman in the millwrights business persuaded my father to leave
home and join up with his firm and he did so and got on by leaps and
bounds till he was one of the best craftsmen in Colchester; and the
Boss died and my father started on his own. Now I should like to
mention how the poor millers existed in those days. First when they
had a load of grist to grind the farmers had no scales, they simply sent
word to the mill and the millers went round with the cart, and they
crammed the sacks as full as possible; but when they went back if
they had weighed them they would have found very often 10 or
12 stone short, meal being more bulky than grain. They never
worried as at that time they were very prosperous.

'This reminds me of an old tale round here years ago. A miller
having a bit of a quarrel with a customer, to every question he
answered, "I don't know." At last in desperation he asked him,

"What do you know," and he answered, "Millers always have plenty of fat pigs, but I don't know whose food they eat." '

The miller led a hard life in days gone by; he had to work when the wind blew, irrespective of hours, and often he used to sleep in his mill just as some of the windmillers in Brittany did until almost the present day; and at Hawkinge smock mill, Kent, the miller's dog would wake the boys when the bell alarm rang at night. Of old the miller was punished for working on Sunday, although in more modern times, when a protest against Sunday work was made to Mr. Wade of Wicklewood tower mill, Norfolk, he retorted: 'If the Lord is good enough to send me wind on a Sunday, I'm going to use it.'

The miller had to be alert to keep the gap between the stones constant however choppy the wind, and before the days of the centrifugal governor this was done by hand. He had to watch the power of the wind, to judge how much sail cloth to spread, and to be prepared to stop the mill under sail and either take in or let out more cloth, for there were then no patent sails. And before the fantail came into use he had to watch the direction of the wind as well and keep the sails square into the wind's eye. The miller had to be able to undertake his own running repairs; a few indeed could undertake all except major work and many dressed their stones themselves, a regular and tedious job, taking several days if done properly. All this, of course, can still be seen on the Continent, although most millers have some auxiliary power. Not every mill had such help, however, in the days of steam engines and horse traction, and a long calm was as bad for trade as a heavy storm was for the mill.

At Alford, Lincolnshire, over forty years ago, there lived Lot Ward who used to tramp out to preach at most of the villages within a seven-mile radius of the town. He had the reputation of being a good trencherman and, after delivering his discourse, of seeking hospitality where the best table was kept. At Addlethorpe the house he sought was that of Mr. Chambers, who had Addlethorpe windmill and bakery at the time, and after one of his services Lot Ward knocked at the Chambers' door. 'Peace unto this house and all in it,' said Lot when the door opened. 'Brother Chambers, I would have prayer with thee.' 'Just the man we want, Lot,' said Chambers who was a bit of a wag. 'We've had no wind for three weeks; come in and pray for wind.' Lot led the way to the parlour, pulled Mr. Chambers down on to his knees and prayed:

The Miller

'O Lord! send wind and relieve our poor brother,' which might have been expressed differently; and when prayers and a good meal were finished, stumped back to Alford.

In the early hours of the following morning Mr. Chambers awoke and realised that the wind was blowing. Getting up, he dressed, went into the mill, started up and ground until his man arrived; and for five days and nights they kept the mill at work without stopping. At the end of this time they had ground all the grist in the mill and needed time to deliver it and collect more; so Mr. Chambers sent a post card addressed simply, 'Lot Ward, Alford', and on the other side wrote, 'Had enough wind, dakker it a little' (i.e. let it up a bit).

Milling and baking could not by law be combined in medieval times, but for the last one hundred and fifty years or more it has been a common enough combination. In this connection a miller with a bakehouse not far from Addlethorpe received a printed instruction during the war from the Ministry of Food that to save flour, baking tins were not to be dusted with it before the dough was put in. In reply he wrote: 'In this bakehouse we are so careful that every time we catch a fly we shake the flour off its feet before we let it go.'

At Littleworth Common tower mill, Oxfordshire, the last miller's brother, when a boy, used to play the fiddle while taking round the grist cart and Noah Edwards, the last miller of Arkley tower mill, Hertfordshire, if there was no wind, would sit on the fan stage of a fine evening and play his fiddle.

But the queerest miller in the traditions of the Sussex Downs was Master Coombs, whose boast it was that his antique little mill, not far from Newhaven, had belonged to his ancestors from the days of Henry VIII. He once made a strong assertion as to a statement he had put forth, that if it were not true, he would never enter his mill again. Upon the statement being proved incorrect, he kept his word. He would spend hours every day upon the upper step of the mill stairs, but never to the end of his life did he enter the building. One of his freaks was the painting of his mill horse. The hues varied frequently. One week a whole market town would be startled by an animal which was pea green; next month it would be blue—then rose pink. Perhaps someone had told him of the chameleon. His marriage scarcely came up to his ideal, and in expansive moments he owned that this was in a measure his own fault, 'For,' he said, 'as I was a gooin' across Excete Lane to be married at Denton Church, I heard a voice from Heaven a-saying unto me—"Willyam Coombs! Willyam Coombs! if so be that you marry Mary Bridges, you'll always be a miserable man!" And so I've always found it,' he added, 'and I be a miserable man.' [1]

There was also disaster.[2] In Halesworth churchyard is a stone commemorating 'Edward Swan, who lost his life by a Windmill's falling down Jany. 12th, 1762. Aged 56 years.' The *Ipswich Journal* of 16th January, 1762, contains this paragraph: 'Last Monday night the mill of Mr. Swan of Halesworth was blown down; Mr. Swan, who was in it, had his arms and legs broken, and his skull fractured in such a manner that he died soon after.'

Nearly a century later a similar accident deprived another miller of life, as witness a headstone in Cookfield churchyard for:

'John Bier, who died 13th February, 1860, Aged 39 years.

> Appointed 'tis for all to die
> And death to him came suddenly,
> A loving husband, father dear,
> Such was the man lies buried here,
> A wife and seven children left behind,
> The world to try and friends to find.'

The *Ipswich Journal* (18th February, 1860) contains an account of the inquest held at the King's Head, Cookfield. A neighbour told how he saw Bier on the steps of the mill situated on a small eminence on the left-hand side of the road leading from Bury to Lavenham. The mill was going fast in a strong wind and shaking to and fro. Suddenly there was a crack; the post which supported the whole mill had broken off at a knot in the wood (oak), and the whole structure tumbled down, the sails falling into the road. Today Cookfield folk still speak of 'Mill Corner', although the post mill of the name disappeared ninety years ago.

J. E. Saunders, born in 1844, describes vividly [3] an experience in the old post mill in which he started his career.

'Pollock mentions among the pleasures of his boyhood "The voice

[1] M. A. Lower, *Contributions to Literature*, 1854.

[2] *East Anglian Daily Times*, 3rd September, 1940.

[3] *The Reflections & Rhymes of an Old Miller*, by J. E. Saunders, London, Hodder & Stoughton, n.d.

of tempest heard secure"; and this was a feeling which occasionally gave me great enjoyment at the old windmill. When a storm was brewing, I generally let her run as long as I could. Then I had to stop and take some cloth off. Often I was only just in time; and there was a strange exhilarating delight when I got back in the dry and took off my dripping coat, to hear the storm beating on the boards outside while I was back in shelter, and all was safe.

'But it was not always so pleasant up there, and like everything else it had its drawbacks as well as its advantages. Many a time during these years when I was out shifting the cloths in a storm, the water has run off them down my arms and out at my trouser legs. Of course, there was no chance of getting dry clothes until I went home; and in the winter they have sometimes been frozen on me for hours.

'I can only once remember being frightened by a storm when I was at the old windmill; all other times I took it as part of my work, without any sense of alarm, and I recall that my father was particularly amused and, I suppose, pleased by being told by a man he met one day at market that I was "not a bit scared" by a burst of bad weather that had caught the mill the night before.

'The time I was afraid was some two years after, and I can only write of it haltingly and imperfectly, for it was an experience I never have and never shall forget. It was in October or November, at a time when I was so busy that I had not kept a proper look out for storms, which we always reckoned to do in wild weather, and a tremendous hurricane caught me unawares. My first warning was that the mill was running faster and faster, but I was not really disturbed then until I had put the brake on and gone down to take some cloth off. Outside it was as black as pitch. I felt my way round to one sail and was just beginning to uncloth when the gale came on like mad. It blew me up against the roundhouse, and away went the sails as if there was no brake on at all.

'I shall never forget how I rushed back up the ladder. The whole mill rocked so that the sacks of meal that were standing in the breast were thrown down like paper, but I got to the brake lever somehow and threw all my weight on it. But it hardly seemed to check her. I knew that if the brake was kept on she was bound to catch fire, so I let it off, and round she went, running at such a rate that the corn flew over the top and smoke blinded and suffocated me.

'Then I was frightened. I expected her to crash over at any

moment, and half overcome by the smoke and din I dashed down the ladder and out into the close. But no sooner had I got there than I thought it was cowardly to run away, so I went back to have another try to stop her. By this time the light had gone out but I got up into the stone floor and once more put the brake on, this time jumping on the lever and putting my shoulders under the next floor so that I could prize it down with all my strength. The sparks were flying out all round the brake as she groaned and creaked with the strain, but it still did not stop the sails, and I doubt whether anything could had not the hurricane itself subsided as suddenly as it sprang up.'

While fantails may prevent storm damage from the wind, lightning is a factor that must be reckoned with as the following accounts will show. The first is contained in a letter from Mr. Blackman, a well-known Sussex millwright, to the late Mr. K. J. Tarrant. 'About 1890 I had an alarming experience at Silverhill Mill, St. Leonards. My brother-in-law and myself had been new gearing the spur wheel and were anxious to complete to get home by the evening train, a violent thunderstorm came on about 2 p.m. The lightning increased in vividness. Several flashes appeared to come direct on the quants, with a sharp report like the crack of a hunting whip, getting worse. We left the wheel, and went into the warehouse adjoining the round-house, and sat on some sacks of wheat. Soon a blinding flash and report, like a heavy gun, with clouds of dust and smoke made us run to the house of the miller. On our return sometime after, we found that the top of the upright sweep had been struck by lightning, the current running down the connecting rod of the sweep, cutting asunder all the cast iron cranks of the shutters on that sweep passing into the mill through the round beam (windshaft) to the sack tackle and down the sack chain. The end of this was about one foot from the floor, from this to the iron tongues in the floor, ripping some out, then on to the bell wire at the entrance door, it threw the bell pull across the road about 35 feet, and when we could look round we found that the links of the sack chain were welded for about 3 feet, so that we could hold it out like a rod—on examination of the cranks to the shutters, where each one was broken, a globule of molten iron was on the fracture—and this in an instant of time!!

'A barn and farm buildings were set on fire, and what with the shouts of the people and firemen, the cries of the pigs and noise of the cattle; *with our narrow escapes*, made it extremely uncanny.'

The Miller

The second is from a contemporary copy of *The Mechanics Maga-zine* containing a vivid account of the destruction of Toothill Mill (between Epping and Ongar in Essex) by lightning on 18th June, 1829. This account is very similar to the experience related by Mr. Blackman, and by a strange coincidence, the mill was again struck June 1928, exactly ninety-nine years later, though it was derelict at the time and the damage was consequently of little account.

In 1829 'the discharge struck one of the sweeps in the centre where the sail was fastened to the stock with an iron collar and bolt. It passed down the sail into the windshaft, riving the timbers and dis-lodging the opposite sail completely. Entering the mill by the shaft, the current failed to find a satisfactory conductor, and the damage to the crown (brake) wheel, wallower and other gear was tremendous, and the whole of the roof was flung off and scattered over a wide area. Finding the sack chain, it travelled down, welding the links in its passage, but on the first floor it became diverted to the iron sack weights. Those it flung in all directions, and the damage to the floor and walls was very severe. An exit was found by way of the metal roof of the roundhouse, whence a short leap to the iron braces at the foot of the stairs completed its destructive journey. The miller was found shockingly maimed and blackened, and one leg had to be amputated. Splinters of wood and grains of wheat had penetrated his skin at all points, and during his months of convalescence more than a cupful of grain was extricated'. Mr. Isaac Taylor made a lithograph of the damaged mill, and the sale of copies helped in large measure to pay for the restoration of the mill.

The late Mr. William Warren, the Hawkhurst millwright, was trimming the cogs in the tail wheel of a post mill with his brother Frank when it was struck by lightning. The mill was undamaged, but the chisel flew out of his hands, which were numbed for some time afterwards, and he described it as though the shaft had been struck with a hammer.

On a roof timber in Haughley post mill, Suffolk, was a note:

'Harry Sore Haughley, aged 18 in February 1884, at this time of the year 1884 there was an earthquake when Harry Baker was miller and Harry Sore was carter and it stopped the mill which Harry Sore was clothing £10,000 damage was done in England.'

This is a record of the famous Colchester earthquake, but accidents were not always from natural causes, as is shown by the following

The Men

extract from a letter to me from Mr. John Bryant.

'There was another old post mill in the parish of Gt. Bromly, about 4½ miles from my home, which was destroyed about the same time; I will tell you a curious tale about it. There was a large pond on one side of the mill reaching within a foot of the ladder when her head was due North; they had to push the mill round to keep her head to wind which was a tiring job. We had to gear the brake wheel and the landlord decided he would have a fly tackle (fantail) fixed at the same time, so we built one and fixed it when we had close on finished the wheel. We worked very late one night as they were crying out for meal and the tenant, a good sort, went and fetched us a ½ gallon of beer and a loaf of bread and some onions and stayed up looking at our job. When we had nearly finished he took his lantern and bid us good night; during the time he had been talking to us the wind had shifted and the ladder was right on the edge of the pond, so the poor old fellow stepped off the ladder right into the pond. We heard him yell out and rushed down and got him out. He had forgotten the fly tackle and we were too busy on our job to think of reminding him; but he never suffered from this cold bath.'

Another miller got a ducking for a different reason, as told to me by Mr. John Saunderson, the Louth millwright. Tickler's post mill at Withern, Lincolnshire, stood in the yard of the water mill beside the mill dam. While corn was being hoisted into the mill one of the quarterbars gave way and the mill collapsed into the dam; Mr. Tickler escaped and Mr. Saunderson pulled out the windshaft assembly later.

When Ramsden Heath post mill, Essex, collapsed in about 1878, Mr. Agnis, later of Mountnessing post mill, Essex, saw it happen from Billericay post mill. The miller was in the mill at the time, and Agnis rushed to the scene, sawed away timbers and extricated the miller unhurt; but his hair turned grey with shock.

At the close of the day the old-fashioned miller used to set the sails of his mill at an angle representing St. Andrew's cross to equalise the strain on them; in the morning before starting work, however, he set them to represent St. George's cross. It was an act of worship, which was supposed to bring good luck to the day's work and was called 'millers' pride'; and when a neighbouring miller passed away all the millers in the neighbourhood set the sails of their mills to the St. George's cross.

The Air whistles round him as keen as a knife,
He finds out its beating and round the Mill goes.
    Let the wind ſhift as 'twill,
    He steadies his Mill,
He has but to peep out and follow his nose,
Still whirling and twirling he lives without ſtrife.
He veers to the wind and its changes he knows.
But how ſhould he ſteady a whirligig Wife,
When the Devil can't find out which way the wind blows.
    Whirling twirling &c.

FIG. 61. MILLER'S SONG FROM 'A FRIEND IN NEED', BY MICHAEL KELLY, 1797.

XX. REMOVALS

'I have seen many things which I trust to tell you one day, also the muckle kirk of this place; and all around the city are mills whilk havena muckle wheels nor mill-dams, but gang by the wind—strange to behold.'—SIR WALTER SCOTT, Jeanie Deans in *The Heart of Midlothian*.

THE laws of Oleron, adopted in this country about 1314, decided that it was illegal to move a mill unless this was done by the lord of the manor, although in 1820 a mortgaged post mill in Norfolk was adjudged a chattel and moved.

Bennett and Elton quote the moving of a mill by the Abbot of Meaux from Beforth to Drynghow in the parish of Skipsea some time between 1372 and 1396 and an order in the reign of Charles I that a windmill that formerly stood on Monthill, Middlesex, be brought back again.

The moving by capstan in 1768 of a mill at Bromley, Kent, a distance of four hundred yards at the rate of four yards a day by Sir Charles Peers is also mentioned, as well as the removal in about 1790 of the post mill from Hale Bank to Hale, near Liverpool, with a team of thirty-eight horses, commemorated by the rhyme.

> They've moved the wooden mill
> To the Brow of Sandy Hill,
> According to contraction.
>
> If the miller we can trust
> Now we'll have a crust
> To our satisfaction.

There is a well-known painting of the removal of a post mill at Brighton, which is inscribed:

'This mill was drawn from the spot now called Regency Square to Preston (a distance of two miles) on the 28th March, 1797, by eighty six oxen which belonged to the following gentlemen:

W. Stanford Esq.	Mr. Trill.
Mr. Hodson,	Mr. Hall.
Mr. Henshar.	Mr. Hardwicke.
Mr. Serace.	

The expedition was commanded by
Mr. T. Hodson.'

xxva. Pakenham Mill, Suffolk, still at work.

xxvb. Cattell's Mill, Willingham, Cambridgeshire, built 1828, and still at work.

xxvc. Stevens' Mill, Burwell, Cambridgeshire, still at work.

xxvd. Billingford Mill, Norfolk, built 1860 on the site of a post mill and still at work.

xxvib. Herringfleet drainage mill, Suffolk, still at work.

xxvid. Stallingborough Mill, Lincolnshire, built 1875 and still at work.

xxvia. St. Olaves drainage mill, Suffolk, built 1910 and still at work.

xxvic. Skidby Mill, Yorkshire, built 1821 and still at work.

xxvii*a*. Outwood post mill, Surrey, built 1665 and still at work.

xxvii*b*. Cat and Fiddle Mill, Dale Abbey, Derbyshire, dated 1788 and still at work.

xxvii*c*. Great Chishill Mill, Cambridgeshire, built 1819 and worked occasionally.

xxvii*d*. Woolpit Mill, Suffolk, still at work.

xxviii*a*. North Leverton Mill, Nottinghamshire, still at work.

xxviii*b*. Bidston Mill, Wirral, Cheshire, preserved.

xxviii*c*. Friston Mill, Suffolk, still at work.

xxviii*d*. Cross-in-Hand Mill, Sussex, moved from Uckfield in 1855, still at work.

XXIX. Trade card of William Leach of the
snuff mills, Devizes, Wiltshire.

xxx. John Bryant, the Colchester millwright, by A. van Anrooy.

XXXI. Tombstone at Wiveton, Norfolk, to Thomas Smith, millwright, d. 1725.

xxxii. The white lead mill belonging to Samuel Walker & Co., taken from the garden of the Rosemary Branch Tea Gardens, Islington, from the original water colour.

Removals

Other removals in Sussex include Fishbourne post mill, said to have been moved from Littlehampton, ten miles away, on a trolley in the 1850's;[1] Rusper Mill from Cripplegate, London, in 1810; Blackboys post mill (built 1818) from Glynde with horses in 1868; and Cross-in-Hand, which was twice moved, first from Mount Ephraim, Uckfield, in 1855 to Cross-in-Hand and secondly in 1868 to its present site, by Medhursts the Lewes millwrights.

In Kent, Coles Finch [2] lists a large number of removals, including some into Sussex and some from that county; all seem to have been smock mills except a post mill built at Rye, moved to Appledore, back to Rye and finally to Appledore again. Two mills were moved from Alkham and Folkestone to Ringwould in 1819 and to Bethersden respectively, the latter on three trucks by a traction engine. A Petham mill was moved to Stelling Minnis on a six-wheeled trolley by horses and the road had to be widened en route to let it pass. Warren, the Hawkhurst millwright, moved a mill from Gun Green to Four Throws on rollers, hauled by a bullock team. But Coles Finch is incorrect in stating that Lympne Mill was moved from Cheriton on farm wagons and that one was moved by barge from Hythe to Ruckinge. Salt Hill Mill, Slough, Buckinghamshire, was bought for £100 in 1848 and moved by barge to Chatham and thence to Luton by Henry Paine and Sons, the millwrights, for £80. The corner posts were sawn down the centres and were bolted together again with tarred twine packing between the sections. A move omitted by Coles Finch is that of the post mill at Chinnor, Oxfordshire, from Chatham, also by barge.

Among windmills moved in Essex, Sible Hedingham post mill was taken to a new site on rollers moved by crowbars, and in Bucks, Lacey Green smock mill was moved from Chesham in 1821. In Cambridgeshire, Six Mile Bottom post mill was moved in 1846 when the railway was built and an interesting inscription on a plate in Madingly Mill, near Cambridge, reads:

WALTER AMBROSE HARDING OF
MADINGLY HALL CAUSED THIS
WINDMILL TO BE BROUGHT FROM
ELLINGTON IN HUNTINGDONSHIRE
AND TO BE REBUILT HERE ON

[1] Bennett and Elton, Vol. II.
[2] *Watermills and Windmills*, by W. Coles Finch, London, C. and W. Daniel, 1933.

The Men

Mr. Hunt, Soham, Cambridgeshire, moved a post mill from Cheveley to Littleport; he cut the brickwork, removed the post and substructure and jacked the body down in one day, moved the mill on two nine-foot drugs and reversed the process at Littleport.

In Suffolk, Gedding post mill was moved twice. The last time from Felsham in 1867; it was stuck in a water splash en route and had to be left in it overnight. Thorpness post mill, built at Aldringham as a grist mill in 1803, was moved in 1924 and altered to pump water into the water tower. Beddingfield post mill was moved from Oakley on a drug and moved up the field with a horse mole normally used for draining. Tannington post mill was moved from Framlingham on a drug, which broke down on Saxtead Green, while Great Thurlow smock mill is said to have come from Slough, Bucks.

The diary of Thomas King of Thelnetham, Suffolk, refers to several removals on the Norfolk-Suffolk borders:

'Hollands Mill at Thetford, removed whole, should a been only it fell down and smashed to pieces April 1818.

Stanton lower mill removed whole in April 1818.

My old mill went to Diss 1819.

Fordham's Mill, Norton, removed into the Fen in Sept. 1821.

Robert Brooks mill set up at Hopton, came from Bardwell, March 1834.'

Windmills have always been used as landmarks, and as seamarks too. One of the first steeplechases to be run was in 1835 and was won by Captain Becher on Vivian; it had Waddesdon Mill, Bucks, as the starting point. The Tichborne Claimant, at his trial, spoilt his case because he could not remember Owlesbury windmill, Hampshire. Greengrass post mill, Yarmouth, Norfolk, was an old white mill kept painted as a seamark by the Admiralty; it stood on the site of the present coastguard station and was later moved two and a half miles to North Dean.

The body of Banham composite mill (Plate IV) was moved from Hingham on a drug hauled by ten horses; it was to have been

170

erected on top of the ridge, but the drug became bogged and it was decided to build the tower there and erect the mill on it.

In Lincolnshire, several post mills were moved, among them Roving Molly Mill at Hemswell was moved twice, the last occasion being from Blidworth in the 1850's, while Kirkby Green Mill was moved from Digby by Atkin, the Sleaford millwright, in about 1865.

Two Lincolnshire tower mills were moved complete except for their towers; Heckington eight-sailed mill has already been referred to; the other originally stood on Beverly Road, Hull, Yorkshire; it was bought by Charles Foster in 1880, carted to Stone Ferry, loaded on to 'billy boys', which sailed round to Trusthorpe on the Lincolnshire coast, was beached and unloaded and the new tower was built of bricks made close by, by Mr. Foster.

In Hertfordshire, Hine quotes [1] the moving of a mill at Hitchin.

'1820: The windmill standing in the open fields between the Manley Highway and the Offley Road was removed bodily to a new site on the Gaping Hills, a distance of 450 yards. The ground from point to point was cleared and levelled of all fences, banks and ditches, and then the mill, being raised by screw jacks and a frame on four wheels being built under it, was pulled in full working order (stones, machinery, sails and all) by thirty-six horses harnessed in six rows of six abreast. The schools were allowed a holiday to see this wonderful feat.'

Nettlebed smock mill, Oxfordshire, was burned down on the night of Good Friday, 1912, and its destruction prompted Mr. S. Adey Guttridge of Caversham to write: 'It was with mingled feelings that I read the announcement of the demolition of the old windmill of Nettlebed Hill. It is nearly ninety years ago since my father placed it there and set it to work. Perhaps some of your readers will be interested to know that it formerly occupied another position. When first built it occupied a site a little below Watlington, but the owner found it was situated too low to catch sufficient wind to keep it working. He then conceived the idea of moving it to Nettlebed, and for this purpose engaged my father (grandfather of Councillor F. W. Dormer) to carry out the work, he being then a single young man in business as millwright at Wallingford. All machinery etc. being removed, the trunk was placed upon two timber carriages drawn by

[1] *History of Hitchin*, R. L. Hine, London, G. Allen & Unwin, 1929.

16 horses. The journey up Nettlebed Hill was done with great difficulty and arriving at the top both timber carriages broke down, and the mill rolled over and over and stopped just at the place they wanted to fix it. This was done somewhere about the year 1823 or 1824. I have heard the story many times from my father's lips, and I could tell a little sequel to it, but I think I have said enough.'

In Nottinghamshire, Hucknall Sick Club Mill was bought in 1790 from a farmer and moved twice; Tuxford composite mill came from Grassthorpe in 1870 and the mills which at one time stood in a row along the ridge of Nottingham Forest were very widely travelled.

There were thirteen in all, twelve post and one tower mill, seven left-handed and six right-handed 'which to many had a strange appearance and occasionally it was jokingly accounted for that some must be grinding whilst others were ungrinding'.

One of the post mills was brought from Newark to Nottingham Forest and was finally demolished; the tower mill was also dismantled and the remaining post mills were moved as follows to:

Brighton, Sussex.—This was the largest mill which cost £1,000 to build at the beginning of the nineteenth century and was sold for £100 before removal fifty years later. It has not been stated which of several post mills at Brighton this was.

Edwinstowe, Notts.

Farndon, near Newark, Notts.—This had previously been damaged in the 1831 riots.

Blidworth, Notts.—This was 'Roving Molly' already referred to and is said to have been moved on nine wagons.

Kegworth, Leicestershire.

Lenton, Notts.

Newton, Notts.—Pulled down in 1952.

Redmile, Leicestershire.

Strelley, Notts.

A letter to *The Nottingham Journal* [1] stated:

'The men in the different mills tried to score over each other especially when a squall came along. They each tried to hold out longer than his neighbour before stopping to take some cloth off the sails, which at that time were hand cloths. They had to be untied and taken off the bottom of each sail in turn, a very difficult and trying task when it was blowing hard and perhaps raining or snowing. Then when the wind abated, the cloths had to be replaced.

'This would happen many times a day in squally weather and sometimes to avoid leaving the mill the men used the brake and each miller tried to hold out longer than his rivals. But immediately one mill stopped the others followed suit.

'The brake wheels and brake bands were made of wood and my father said that his mill was often filled with smoke caused by the friction. They had to stop or set the mill on fire. In fact many fires were caused when in strong winds the brakes failed to stop the sails.'

A writer to *The Nottinghamshire Weekly Guardian* [1] said: 'There was a public house called *The Dusty Miller*, not far from the present *Vernon Arms*. It was kept by a miller who came in and served customers in his floury dress. I had my drink served by him on several occasions when he had just come from the mill across the way.'

> O the little rusty dusty miller,
> Dusty was his coat,
> Dusty was his colour,
> Dusty was the kiss I got from the miller;
> If I had my pockets,
> Full of gold and siller,
> I would give it all,
> To my dusty miller.
>
> (The tune 'Dusty Miller', 1708.)

XXI. MILLWRIGHTS

A WINDMILL at work—a sailing ship of the land—is surely one of the most beautiful pieces of machinery ever fashioned by man, surpassed only by the sailing ship, equalled only by the soaring glider. One of the greatest triumphs of the old millwrights before the age of steam was the windmill, for it represented a successful attempt to utilise an uncontrolled force of nature, achieved by the aid of crude tools and tackle and the millwright's capacity for overcoming difficulties, and requiring in most cases the greatest ingenuity.

[1] Mr. John B. Riley, 8th September, 1923.

The Men

The millwrights who built these mills and harnessed the wind for the use of man were the ancestors-in-trade of the modern mechanical engineers, and survivals of their work should interest all who delight in the fine achievements of the past; both those who are interested in machinery as well as all those who delight to see a windmill as part of the landscape, whether a storm-battered veteran at rest or a live thing at work still serving man.

Mr. John Bryant, the Colchester millwright (Plate XXX), once wrote to me: 'You will admit millwrighting in the old style was very hard work and poorly paid, for instance I could tell you of my experience one or two items as follows. The mills were situated within a radius of 7 or 8 miles from our shop, there was no transport of any kind; we often used to do the journey on foot and carry anything up to 30 lb. weight of tools and get home by the carriers cart at week ends. Later on, my father got a horse and cart so it was better. The two most narrow escapes I had in my life were as follows. I had to drive over to Mersea windmill one Saturday, I started early, as I had another job in the town to do after dinner, and finished my job about 12 o'clock; the Governor told me there was a heavy tide running and if the water was up to a certain mark on the post not to attempt to cross over. When I arrived at the strand the water missed about an inch of the danger point, there was half a gale blowing and the water was choppy. I should have got over alright, but when I got near the middle some sailors were taking advantage of the high tide and were pulling a barge close in shore. The bomb (boom) of the barge was halfway across the road; my cob refused to go under it and began to run backwards. I jumped out of the cart and seized his head but he pulled me down on to my knees; the sailors ran to my assistance and we got past. If he had gone back another 3 feet we should all have been in the Channel. This was the first start; when the cob got frightened I was wearing a pair of woollen gloves. I tore them off and rammed them in my overcoat pocket with my pipe. I got as far as Peldon Rose and went in and had a good stiff glass of rum as I was wet through up to the waist; I started off home and about a mile further on I had to cross a common. I smelled something burning; I looked round but could see nothing wrong, but I went to get my handkerchief out and it was smouldering. I jumped out of the cart pulled off my overcoat and the lining was the same; I stamped it out and for a few minutes I felt dazed. First nearly drowned and then

174

burnt, but I was home soon after 3 o'clock, had a wash and a change of clothes and went on and did my other job at Layer where there was a post mill. Another surprise awaited me; I had to get an engine into position ready for work on the Monday morning, it was a 12 H.P. portable weighing about 4 tons, I had got to shift it about 100 yards. The driver had a beautiful pair of horses and I stood directing him to the exact spot to line up with my drive when I saw the ground giving way. I shouted to him "Quick ahead, the ground is giving way", just in time; the horses bounded forward and just cleared by about 2 feet with their heads jammed right up against the mill door, we had to unharness the horses and take the shafts off before we could get the horses out. Within ½ an hour the ground caved in, it was an old dead well, which must have been covered over close on a hundred years. I began to think I had had enough excitement for one day; considering the well was 10 feet across it was a marvel. We went and had some refreshment and then home for a rest.'

No wonder some of them drank!

Mr. Thomas Hunt, the Soham millwright, told me how, when working at Manea six-sailed tower mill in Cambridgeshire before 1914 when there was no 'closing time', he had to chase one of his men out of a public house at 10 o'clock in the morning and kept him hard at work until 8 p.m. Apparently psychic rather than 'spiritual' forces sometimes took a hand in impeding the millwrights' work, for I was assured that at Weston-on-the-Green, near Bicester, when the millwrights started to build a new mill on an existing mound the structure kept on partially collapsing. Eventually the mound was excavated and the remains of Cromwellian soldiers with coins of the period were found; the mound is now grown over with trees.

While on the subject of graves it may be mentioned that Mr. Scott, the millwright of Radwinter, Essex, had his coffin made from the post of a windmill, and at Wiveton, Norfolk, there is a tombstone (Plate XXXI) with representations of a saw, a pair of dividers, a mill bill and thrift, a dressed millstone and an axe, and bearing the inscription:

> Here Lyeth the Body of Thom[s]
> Smith Millwright he departed
> this life April y[e] 16 in 1725
> Aged 82 years.

and no doubt he died in his bed. But risks there were, and in November 1904 the death was announced[1] of Thomas Rowney Wilkinson, millwright of King's Lynn, Norfolk, resulting from an accident at Massingham post mill in the previous June.

'He was on the mill sail taking out an old whip to put in a new one, and on completing the work told the men to let go. But the sails got out of balance and the lower sail, flying up, his leg was caught between the head of the mill and the sail and he was suspended head downwards. The (safety) chain had not been hooked on to the brake (wheel) properly. He was released after half an hour's work in cutting away the top of the mill, but his leg was terribly crushed.' An action was heard in the King's Lynn County Court arising out of the accident and the miller, Mr. Buckingham, died of heart failure in the following March.

At Thornton Mill in the Fylde the father of Dick Blezzard, the Preston millwright, having examined the sails, said that they were rotten and might fall at any time; while the owner was strenuously denying this one dropped with a crash into the mill yard.

Some years ago Mr. Bryant sent me 'Some of the Events of my Life that occurred to me on my 75th Birthday of the Ups and Downs of the old-type Millwrights', and one of them concerned a narrow escape.

'I went to fit new triangles to the sails at Gt. Holland Mill near Clacton one day and I wanted a 25 stave ladder to reach the sails as they had to swing over the steam mill and granary; being just after harvest time they could not borrow one as they were all busy thatching in that district, so I climbed round the cap of the mill with all my load and climbed out on to the sails. I was busy fitting up my job when suddenly the vanes struck to, jamming my hands and one leg, so I was wedged in, and a good job too as the mill started and I was whirled round. The baker saved my life, he was looking out of the bakehouse window and saw the mill moving off. Knowing I was working on the sails he rushed out and ran up the mill and dropped the brake; but when the mill stopped I was hanging head downwards. He done nobly; he climbed out on the cap to see where I was and shouted out, but he could not get any response from me as my breath was gone for about five minutes. Then I realized my desperate position; I told him to be sure not to strike the vanes back or I

[1] *The Miller*, 7th November 1904.

should fall out, but to turn the mill so as I was right way up. And he was a brick, after I got the right way up he helped me out and I got to the ground. Then I felt bad and they rushed and got me a drop of brandy; that night I drove home 16 miles with the reins attached to my elbows. The Boss that done all the mischief had got delirium tremens and died soon after in Ipswich Jail.'

The late Mr. Bob Martin, one of a family of millwrights of Beccles, Suffolk, once described the replacement of a post in Benhall Mill. The post was made from timber grown on the estate and axed and adzed out; the pintle, which sockets into the crowntree, was of oak, let into the top of the post and side-pinned after the post was set upright. The mill was stripped and everything was taken out of it, the buck was shored up with four poles; they dug down and removed the old post intact and after putting in the new post reversed the process. A similar job was done at Great Chishill Mill, Cambridgeshire (Plate XXVII), in 1870, the timber for the post coming from Brandon, Suffolk.

To Evans, the Bungay millwright, who had two thumbs on his left hand, were apprenticed Mr. Martin's great-grandfather and Si Nunn. The latter, another well-known Suffolk millwright, used a tricycle and once, while dressing the stones at Benhall Mill, to keep people from tampering with the tricycle he tied it to a mill sail and turned the sail up. Mr. Martin had a wooden rope block which had once been on Lord Nelson's 'Victory'; I mentioned this to the late Mr. Dick Blezzard, the millwright of Preston, Lancashire, and he told me that when the old wooden windshaft in Thornton Mill was replaced with an iron one in 1895 or 1896 it was sold to a company which had been formed to make relics from the timbers of the Foudroyant, Nelson's old flagship, which had been wrecked at Blackpool. It was no unusual occurrence for a mill to be struck by lightning and Mr. Blezzard once got a shock from the iron windshaft which made him leap through the brake wheel (or 'wind wheel' as he called it). Finally John Bryant's account of another of his experiences in the 1880's well deserves to be set down here, although it concerns a tide mill and not a windmill.

'I shall never forget when I was at an old watermill worked by the tide at Barrow Hill, Abridge, near Maldon; I was fitting it up with silk dressing machinery and elevators and I lodged in the mill house, which was situated about 500 yards away, and you had to walk along the sea wall to the mill. There was a young man, apprentice, living at the house and it was his spell to work the mill when the tide was down. It was a terrible dark and stormy night and he seemed a bit nervy so he asked me to go down with him for company. As we were old chums I agreed. We took some bread and cheese and I went and got ½ a gallon of porter so we could have our supper when the tide was down. We sat down on a couple of bags of bran and were having quite a pleasant time when there was a terrific crash, and the whole floor of the mill seemed to heave up and the old mill shook and groaned. It put the wind up us for a time, but we plucked up courage enough to lift up the large door in the floor and found the tide had risen within 3 in. of the joists of the floor; but we both agreed we had had enough for one night, so took our old horn lantern and went home to bed. In the morning the problem was solved, the sea was full of porpoises and we came to the conclusion that a large one was chasing the fish down the channel under the mill and when he rose struck the mill floor, so we satisfied ourselves on that point. But I must admit although I had some rough experience, there were times when we had quite a bit of fun.'

XXII. DECLINE

'He lives at Woodbridge in Suffolk, and has just bought some land on the skirts of the little town, to save the Windmill thereon, that otherwise would have been pulled down. Doesn't that show him to be one of the right sort?'—KEENE writing on Edward Fitzgerald.

WHAT has killed the windmill? The broad answer is the Industrial Revolution; but this at first savours too much of the abstract and some more concrete examples may well be set down here.

The steam engine may be quoted as the primary cause, for as a result of the use of steam power the towns increased in size and drained the population of the countryside to fill their factories. Flour mills driven by steam power were built, the earliest being Albion Mill, Blackfriars, equipped with a Boulton and Watt engine and built in 1784; these served the towns, cutting out the small country millers. As the towns grew the countryside became gradually depopulated, less land was put under the plough because of the greater difficulty of obtaining cheap labour, and more land was put down to grass, because of the smaller number of men required to tend sheep and cattle and the increased demand for their products. Grain was imported in increasing quantities and was increasingly dealt with at the ports and the largest centres of consumption and its products distributed by rail all over the country.

Then came the portable steam engine, which enabled farmers to drive their machinery by power, and put down stones to grind their own grist. A further blow came with the introduction of roller milling in the 1870's and the establishment of the large port mills of the present day. But the old millers believed in stone ground flour as exemplified by an amusing obituary notice of 1908. 'Markin, On May 11 Hannah Matilda died in her 87th year, wife of the late W. E. Markin, stone flour miller, Snape. Established 1800. No rollers.' The producer gas plant and the gas engine were further competitors of the wind; but both these and the portable steam engine needed too much attention to kill the windmill of themselves. The solid injection oil engine lent a hand and after 1918 the easy distribution of its fuel by road, combined with the comparative lack of attention which it requires, did as much as anything to take the small country gristing trade from the windmiller. In 1916 the restrictions on flour production put the majority of windmillers out of this side of the business, nor could they recover after the war, for the large flour mills were now able to distribute flour by motor transport to areas hitherto closed to them. The electricity grid, the steel disk mill and other modern machines bought by the farmer also contributed their share, and all this without the additional problem of labour. The wind, though free, is not on tap, and is often not available when it is most wanted. It is changeable and varies in force, and even with patent sails, automatic fantail and governors for the stones, the windmill needs constant attention. Men now would only work between specified hours and those men available were mostly the older ones; the young ones, with few exceptions, preferred to work in or near the towns where, if the cost of living was higher so also were the wages, and there was more amusement to be had. During the war, trained men, both millers and millwrights, went away and never came back, young ones could not be trained, and I have even heard of a factory inspector who threatened to have a windmill closed because it could not be brought into line with modern factory requirements. Mills used for draining the Fens became almost extinct, having been superseded by oil engines driving turbine pumps, or having been left high and dry as the draining operations caused the Fens to shrink, and the only marsh mills at work in any number were now in the Broads district.

During the 1939–45 war the conditions of the previous war were again experienced and after its close the shortage and high price of materials and skilled labour made it virtually impossible to undertake major repairs. The number of mills working by wind was reduced from about three hundred and fifty in 1919 to fifty in 1946 and to twenty-one at the time of writing, and the number of millwrights willing and able to make and put up mill sails in the traditional manner from twelve to three.

As instances of the way in which windmills have disappeared it may be mentioned that in the Chatham and Rochester districts eighty or ninety years ago there were upwards of fifty working windmills; there are now none. In 1926 there were forty-eight working corn mills in East and West Suffolk alone; in 1939 there were fourteen; today there are but four, and only the tower mill at Pakenham (Plate XXV), the mill familiar to millions on the television screen, is working with four sails.

It seems, therefore, that we must make haste to record and preserve while yet we can for the benefit of those who follow us as well as for the interest to ourselves. Recording can be divided into five categories in order of popularity:

> Photographic.
> Historical.
> Technical.
> Measured drawings.
> Scale models.

Photographic records of the exteriors of those mills that remain in all stages of disuse are fairly complete; what are now badly needed are copies of old photographs of mills which have disappeared. I have myself literally retrieved such photographs from the scrap heap and from the waste-paper basket—in both cases in Lincolnshire.

The historical side can be covered by degrees by students of local history, both individually and at summer schools, but the work needs prompt initiation and co-ordination and a steady continuance if useful results are to be obtained.

Technically, a few people, myself included, have been steadily recording (Fig. 45), accumulating and collating data and interior photographs of windmills, which will probably be as complete as they ever can be by the end of the present decade.

Since the war a few architects and engineers have taken a great deal of time and trouble to add to the two or three measured drawings of English windmills that already existed (Fig. 37) and it is to be hoped that increasing numbers of drawings will be made, especially by students.

A few very accurate working models of windmills exist. The finest of all is of course the one-to-twelve scale model of Sprowston post mill, Norwich, made by the late H. O. Clark and now in the Science Museum, and it is hardly likely to be surpassed. My own firm was responsible for the one-to-thirty-six scale model of Bourn post mill, Cambridgeshire, in the Children's Gallery of the Science Museum. This scale is too small for any interior details and what are now wanted are model engineers willing to make accurate scale working models from such drawings as already exist, and not 'free lance' models, which, though they be of superb craftmanship, are useless as records.

From time to time, before and during the first quarter of the present century, a number of private individuals attempted to preserve windmills as landmarks, working or otherwise, and I believe that Bidston tower mill, Birkenhead (Plate XXVIII), was the first to be preserved in this way by Mr. Hudson, of soap fame, in 1894.

But it was not until 1929 that any co-ordinated effort was made; in the summer of that year the *Daily Mail* interviewed the late Mr. A. R. Powys, Secretary to the Society for the Protection of Ancient Buildings, and asked what the Society was doing to protect and preserve windmills. The answer at that time was 'nothing', but the publicity given aroused so much interest that by 1931 a Windmill Section of the Society had been formed.

Although continuously hampered by lack of funds the Windmill Section, first under Miss Batten and Miss Helen Lloyd, and now under Mrs. M. Dance, has achieved results out of all proportion to its membership by giving technical advice, drafting appeals, collecting money and contributing from its very slender resources towards the cost of preservation; collecting and collating information, publishing works, holding exhibitions and awarding certificates 'for zeal in the preservation of these beautiful structures'. It has collaborated with County Councils which have interested themselves in preserving windmills, of which Essex County Council was the first and Kesteven County Council the latest, and with the Ancient Monuments Department of the Ministry of Works which has, under its present Chief Inspector, taken over guardianship firstly of Berney Arms drainage mill, Norfolk (Fig. 42), and secondly Saxtead Green post mill, Suffolk. But perhaps the individual achievement of which the Society can be proudest is trying to keep in working order the Outwood post mill, Surrey (Plate XXVII), built in 1665, and still the oldest working windmill in the country. This was first undertaken in 1931 by organising a vigorous public appeal and again in 1953 with a very substantial grant from the Society's own small funds, the financial aid of the Surrey County Council and the generous help of the Friendship-in-Repair Fund of America and the New York Community Trust. In spite of all this help, however, it is still, at the time of writing, minus two sails. In 1931 too, Bourn Mill, Cambridgeshire, the oldest surviving post mill, was bought, repaired and presented to the Cambridge Preservation Society by Sir Alfred Bossom, M.P., and Mr. Mansfield Forbes (Figs. 59 and 60). The probability is that in another ten or twenty years the only windmills remaining will be derelicts, converted into houses, or preserved through the efforts of private persons, societies, local authorities and the Ministry of Works, and I hope that these efforts will receive practical support and encouragement, both material and moral, from all who read this book.

Appendixes

APPENDIX A

THE ANNULAR SAIL

BY F. C. JOHANSEN, D.Sc.

The torque, or turning effort, due to an element of area of a windmill sail is equal to the product of the tangential component of the wind force on the element multiplied by its radial distance from the axis of rotation. The wind force is approximately proportional to the square of the speed of the wind relative to that of the elemental area of sail; and since in general the speed of the natural wind increases with height above ground level, the average turning force during one revolution of an elemental area increases with the radius at which the element revolves. Hence, from the standpoints both of force and radius arm, the turning effort of a windmill sail is increased by concentrating as much as practicable of the sail area at the greatest possible distance from the windshaft.

In the case of the annular sail (Plate XVI), this was done by providing a large total area of sail in the form of an annulus comprising one hundred and twenty blades spaced as closely together as was feasible without causing undue aerodynamic interference (with consequent loss of efficiency) between adjacent blades. At the extreme inner and outer ends of each blade the wind force is necessarily zero, and has a maximum value intermediate between the ends. From this standpoint alone, the individual blades must not be unduly short radially; hence an aspect ratio (i.e. span ÷ chord) of about six, such as was often given to rectangular aircraft wings forty years ago, represents a good compromise. The individual blades of the annular sail seem to have had about these proportions, and to have been circumferentially spaced about one blade-chord apart.

Another point is that if a sail has a big radial length, the pitch (i.e. the angle between the plane of the surface of the sail and the plane of the circle in which it rotates) should vary from the

185

windshaft to the tip to take account of the increase of circumferential speed as radius increases. How far this was achievable with conventional mill sails I do not know, but I imagine it might be so difficult, structurally, as often to be neglected, with consequent loss of aerodynamic efficiency. In the case of the annular sail, however, all the blades were short relatively to the mean radius of the annulus in which they were mounted. Even though, therefore, the pitch of the blades was perhaps constant along their radial length, the consequent loss of efficiency would be small.

The purpose of a windmill is to extract turning power from the wind, and its sails should, therefore, be set at such an angle to the wind direction as to produce the maximum tangential force irrespective of what the associated axial force, or thrust, may be. This angle may need to be small, so that the blade is only slightly inclined to the wind. Now, if a mill has only four sails, each of them must be wide to provide enough area to give the required total turning effort; but it is hardly possible to set wide sails at a small angle to the wind, because they would have to project too far upstream to prevent their trailing edges from touching the body of the mill structure. If the sails are very 'flat' to the wind, the only way in which they can be efficient is for them to rotate at higher speeds than mechanical considerations of mill construction will permit. Hence, the big sails of a four-sailed mill, 'flat' to the wind and rotating slowly, are not efficient and suffer a large thrust in the wind direction which is wasted in friction at the thrust bearing.

The narrow blades of the annular sail, on the other hand, could be inclined at the optimum angle to the wind without projecting inconveniently beyond the plane of the annulus, and could, therefore, work efficiently with small loss from axial friction.

A final feature of the annular sail which may have contributed to its good performance is the uniformity of turning power due to its having a large number of blades equally spaced around an annulus. The interference in wind flow due to the mill body downstream of the annulus continuously affects about one-sixth of the total sail area, and the turning power should, therefore, have been very constant in a steady wind. With a four-sailed mill, on the contrary, the interference of the mill body causes a momentary diminution of turning effort four times per revolution every time a sail passes in front of the body.

Appendix A

To summarise, I consider that the good performance of the annular sail was due to a large number of blades or vanes which could be shaped and set to the wind so as to have good aerodynamic efficiency, and all of them being at the greatest practicable radial distance from the windshaft. Uniformity of turning effort was an additional advantage.

APPENDIX B

THE ICONOGRAPHY OF THE WINDMILL

FIG. 62. ARMS OF SAMPSON

WHILE mill bills called fusils or picks, mill rynds called millinks or fers-de-molines, and millstones were used as devices in heraldry, Bennett and Elton were unable to find a single one relating especially to windmills. There is, however, at least one blazon of the family of Sampson: on a field or a mount vert surmounted by a windmill sable (see Fig. 62), while that of Milnes is; azure a chevron between three windmill sails, crossways or; a mullet for difference. There are also Baxter and Cluee. Arg., four windmill sails conjoined in saltire sa. Twentieth-century grants include windmills to Mills, 1913, Keyworth, 1920, Milner, 1924, and four mill sails to Hawkins, 1917, while windmills are included in the arms of several boroughs and used as signs for a number of public houses.

Appendix B

The best-known trade token bearing a windmill is that of Apple-dore, Kent, dated 1794, and there are probably many others of the eighteenth and nineteenth centuries as yet not collated. The Union of Appledore was a community of farmers and others for the protection of persons, places and things from the attention of thieves and rascals and also to bring them to justice. £10 was the reward paid by this Union for bringing a murderer to justice, £1 for an incendiary, and other offences were in proportion. The Union consisted of ten members who paid 10s. 6d. entrance fee and 2s. 6d. annual subscription. William Peckham, who issued the Appledore Token, was one of them. 'Small in Stature but great in Opinion', he was parish clerk and died in 1845, aged seventy-five years. Peckham on one occasion anticipated a raiding party at his mill. He set upon them suddenly when they arrived and cut the calf off the leg of one man with his sword, and it is recorded that the man died of the wound.[1] *Trade Tokens issued in the Seventeenth Century* [2] lists a number bearing wind-mills as follows.

Cambridgeshire:	Doddington and Wood Ditton.
Kent:	Hollingbourne and Maidstone.
Middlesex:	Shadwell.
Southwark:	Horsley Down and Tooley Street.
Surrey:	Richmond.
Ireland:	Kilkenny.
London:	Seventeen in all, but like that of Kilkenny, which was issued by an innkeeper, it seems doubtful if any were for millers. Two, at Wapping, New Stairs and White Hart Yard, Strand, were for meal men.

In *The Windmill in English Mediaeval Art* [3] Mr. John Salmon, F.S.A., has dealt exhaustively with what may perhaps be called the iconography of the windmill; and I have prepared a condensed list from his excellent paper. All the mills are post mills except where noted otherwise.

[1] *Kent Messenger*, 9th January, 1932.
[2] By George C. Williamson, London, Elliott Stock, 1889, 2 vols.
[3] *Journal British Archaeological Association*, Third Series, Vol. VII, 1941.

Appendix B

King's Lynn, Norfolk. In St. Margaret's Church. To Adam de Walsoken, 1349. Engraved in Germany, it illustrates the mediaeval joke of the stupid miller. He is returning to the mill with a sack of corn to be ground slung over his horse's back. Seeing that the animal is tiring he shoulders the sack himself— but mounts the horse!

CARVINGS IN STONE

Burton, Pembrokeshire. A rebus on the altar tomb of the Wogan family of Milton, c. 1520. It consists of a portion of a windmill with a tun or barrel below it.

Denver, Norfolk. On a tombstone to William Beeton, 1820. A drainage mill.

Friskney, Lincolnshire. On two tombstones, one eighteenth century and one 1928. Friskney Tofts Mill.

Launceston, Cornwall. A carving on the exterior of the south porch of the church, c. 1511. The stupid miller joke.

Milton Abbas, Dorset. The rebus of Abbot William de Middleton, similar to that at Burton. In the south aisle, fifteenth century, on the porch in the Abbott's Hall, 1498, and on Manor Farm Delcome, 1515.

Norwich Cathedral, Norfolk. A boss in the south-west angle of the cloisters, c. 1325. The stupid miller joke.

Rievaulx Abbey, Yorkshire. On a portion of a string course, fifteenth century. A mill with a man and two horses.

CARVINGS IN WOOD

Bishop's Lydeard, Somerset. On a bench-end in the church, sixteenth century. A mill with three birds, a sack of corn and a saddled horse.

Bristol Cathedral. On a misericord, sixteenth century. A mill and a man on horseback.

Hatfield House, Hertfordshire. On a newel of the grand staircase, c. 1610. A mill.

London, Westminster Abbey. In Henry VII's chapel on a misericord, sixteenth century. A mill with a (?) monkey on the steps.

North Cadbury, Somerset. On a bench-end in the church, 1538. A mill.

Stapleford Hall, Leicestershire. In an exterior carving of St. George
and the Dragon, 1633. A windmill on a boat.

Thornham, Norfolk. On a bench-end in the church, fifteenth century. A mill.

Windsor, Berkshire. In St. George's Chapel, on a misericord,
c. 1480. A mill with three sparrows bringing sacks of corn to it.

GLASS

Cambridge, Corpus Christi College. In a window on the hall staircase, *c.* 1600. A mill.

Cambridge, King's College Chapel. In the Founder's Chapel, in two
quarries, dated 1677. Two mills.

    In a quarry brought recently from Eastwell Church, Kent. A
mill.

Clavering, Essex. In a window in the north aisle of the church,
c. 1500. A 'common sail' above St. Christopher's head.

Fairford, Gloucestershire. In the east window of Corpus Christi
Chapel, *c.* 1500. A mill.

Greenford, Middlesex. In two roundels in the north and east windows of the chancel of the church, sixteenth century. Two mills
said to have come from King's College Chapel, Cambridge.

Long Melford, Suffolk. In a roundel in the west window of the south
aisle of the church, *c.* 1490. A mill.

Ludlow, Shropshire. In the north wall of St. John's Chapel in a St.
Christopher window, fifteenth century. A mill.

Shipley, Sussex. In a memorial window to Lady Burrell, 1922.
Shipley smock mill.

Stoke-by-Clare, Suffolk. In a quarry in the south aisle of the church,
c. 1470–1480. A tower mill.

From Westerham, Kent. In a quarry, fourteenth century. A boy
riding a hobby horse and holding a toy windmill.

GRAFFITI

    Examples of seventeenth- and eighteenth-century graffiti are to
be seen on the churches of:

        Gamlingay, Cambridgeshire;
        Long Stanton, Cambridgeshire;
        Tottenhoe, Bedfordshire;
        Wicken, Cambridgeshire;   also
        Melton Gaol, Suffolk, fifteenth century.

Appendix B

Ranworth, Norfolk. On the church screen, early fifteenth century. A toy windmill in the hand of one of the Holy Children.

Torbryan, Devon. On the church screen, fifteenth century. St. Victor of Marseilles, holding a sword in his right hand and a windmill in his left. He was martyred in A.D. 303, by being crushed between two mill stones.

Winchelsea, Sussex. In the court house. A panel painting, c. 1350. St. Leonard blessing the crops with four windmill sails on the end of his crozier.

WALL PAINTINGS

Belton, Suffolk. A painting in the church, of 'The Three Living and the Three Dead', no longer visible, fifteenth century. Two mills, one a tower mill.

Baunton, Gloucestershire. In a painting of St. Christopher on the north wall of the nave of the church, c. 1400. A mill.

Bramhall Hall, Cheshire. In the banqueting hall, c. 1450. A fragmentary painting of the stupid miller joke.

Ditcheat, Somerset. In a painting of St. Christopher on the north wall of the nave of the church, fifteenth century. A mill.

Gawsworth, Cheshire. In a copy of a destroyed painting of St. Christopher in the church, c. 1450. A mill.

Henstridge, Somerset. In a copy of a destroyed painting of St. Christopher in the church, fifteenth century. A mill, a laden packhorse, a dog and a man carrying a sack.

Kersey, Suffolk. In a painting of St. George and the Dragon on the south wall of the nave of the church, fifteenth century. A portion of a mill, very faint.

Rye, Sussex. In a painting of the town in 'The Other House', West Street, sixteenth century. A portion of a mill.

West Grinstead, Sussex. In a copy of a painting of St. Christopher in the church, c. 1520. A portion of a mill.

PLASTERWORK

Denham Court, Bucks. In a landscape piece in the billiard room, 1697. Two mills.

Appendix B

At Mary-in-the-Marsh, Kent. On the base of a chalice in the church.
The maker's mark of a mill in an oval.

Sᵣ Chr· Hilyarde
FULSTOW, 1595.

Tho: Mitchell
MARSHCHAPEL, 1595.

Sᵣ Chr: Hilyarde
MARSHCHAPEL, 1595

FIG. 63. FROM A MAP OF FULSTOW AND MARSHCHAPEL, LINCOLNSHIRE

193

APPENDIX C

BUXHALL WINDMILL CONTRACTS

BY THE LATE H. O. CLARK

THE Buxhall accounts are two in number and refer to two different windmills, the first a smock tower mill built in 1815 and the second a very large brick tower mill built in 1860 (Plate III). The first account is on a somewhat faded piece of thin yellowish paper and is in a good legible hand. It reads thus:

	Mr. Clover			
	To Samuel Wright			
1815		£.	s.	d.
	To building a smock wind Mill as per agreement	520.	15.	11¾.
	To extra studd^g & partitions in wheat bin 88 feet 9 in.	3.	8.	9.
	To large meal hopper cont^g 48 feet	2.	8.	0.
	To a pair of pullie Blocks Iron^d up with Screw Eyes to do.	1.	11.	6.
		528.	3.	5¾.
June 30th	To 2 Shoe Brassis for Nedging		5.	7½.
		528.	9.	1¼.

A point to notice is the contract price ending with 11¾d; a figure more suggestive of the drapery trades. Further, a careful examination shows that the addition is wrong with the result that Mr. Clover still owes Wright 9d. This item for shoe brasses for Nedging refers to another of Mr. Clover's mills, this time a very old water mill, and still standing. It was sold out of the Clover family a few years since, but in an old directory for 1844 we find: 'Isaac Clover yeoman and corn miller'.

The smock mill was the successor to a still older one and there is a reference to it in the *Colchester Gazette* for 16th July, 1814, which runs thus: 'About 10 o'clock on the night of Thursday the newly erected windmill of Mr. Raynham of Buxhall Suffolk was discovered to be on fire and was entirely burnt down. The premises were very recently insured with the Norwich Union Office. On Saturday last Mr. Raynham was committed to Ipswich Gaol on suspicion of wilfully having set fire to Same.'

We do not know what finally happened to Mr. Raynham, but the next year the site was acquired by the Clovers and a new mill built. Wright the millwright was succeeded at Needham Market by one Page, who in turn gave way to Brooks. When he died the place was shut down and most of the connection taken over by Catchpole of Stowmarket; since he died there has been no millwright in the district.

In 1860 it was decided to demolish the smock mill and construct another of greatly increased power, utilising as far as possible the old materials. This work was undertaken on a time and materials basis and the complete accounts are extant and in excellent order. The millwright selected was one William Bear of Sudbury, Suffolk, and in the 1844 Directory he is noticed as being a 'mill wright and machine maker' with his place of business in the parish of Ballingdon on the Essex side of the River Stour.

The materials bill is headed:

> 1860   Mr. Clover   Buxhall.
> To Wm. Bear
> Account of building new mill.

The first entry is dated May 8th, on which date much of the heavy materials was delivered. The following are some of the more interesting items:

		£.	s.	d.
May 8th	18 cast iron bearers to fix in. Wt. 5 cwt. 2 qrs.	4.	o.	o.
„	12 cast iron segments to fix on curbb (curb) 19 cwt.	13.	6.	o.

These castings represent a shade over 14s. per cwt. delivered on the site, which gives an idea of the cost of iron in country districts.

May 8th	15 window frames and sashes primd & glassed with cords and weights	14.	o.	o.

Appendix C

From this it is realised that a very large tower was contemplated to require such a large number of lights. It also shows that, as one would expect, carpentry work shows up cheaply in country districts. The next item of interest:

		£.	s.	d.
May 8th	A pole and trail for bricklayers	1.	0.	0.

It refers to a tall straight pole truly plumbed in the centre of the site from which as a centre the bricklayers revolved a trail or trammel to give a true circle to the work. The length of the trammel was of course shortened as the wall rose in height.

May 8th	Elm crubb (curb) to lay on brickwork 17 ft. 8 in diameter 8¼ 12 framed together in 10 parts with 20¾ duel bolts	10.	0.	0.
,,				

Next follow various items for bolts, anchor plates, nuts, screws, etc., and also the following:

May 8th	4 cast iron chairs and roullers to go under cap not turned up. Wt. 1 ct.		18.	0.
,,	3 large cast iron chairs and rouls to go under neck turned up. Wt. 3 cwt.	3.	6.	0.
,,	6 rauls and 6 chairs for cap turned up. Wt. 2 cwt. 1 qr. 9 lb.	2.	18.	0.
,,	11 inside chairs and roulers fitted up for cap. Wt. 4 cwt. 3 qrs. 12 lbs.	5.	0.	0.
,,	57 nut headed screws sartid 15 lb.		10.	0.

Note the quaint way of spelling the word 'assorted'.

On May 20th a large quantity of timber was delivered and it is interesting as giving an idea of the large scantlings considered necessary in a mill of this large size and also the very low prices prevailing in those days for large stock.

May 20th	2 oak shear trees for cap each 22 ft. long 11 × 11.	9.	7.	0.
,,	Oak headstock 10½ feet long 9 × 6½	1.	3.	0.
,,	3 pieces of oak for hard blocks to frame into headstock. Each 4 ft. long 6 × 15.	1.	16.	0.
,,	Oak weather beam 10 ft. long 6 in. × 20 ins. cut circuel of cap.	2.	10.	0.

		£.	s.	d.
May 20th	Fir crown beam 10 ft. 3 in. long 11 × 11	1.	15.	0.
,,	Oak tail beam 10 ft. long 11 × 11	2.	2.	6.
,,	Outside tail beam 10½ ft. long 10½×6.	1.	3.	6.

All these items are common terms in the millwright's vocabulary and the timbers used are usual.

Next we have material for the cap roof:

			s.	d.
May 20th	Elm curbb for cap contain 40 ft. of timber 5⅛ × 4 cut circular		13.	0.
,,	12 new principal elm spars for cap each 15 ft. long 3½ × 3	2.	18.	0.
,,	Cross peaces to frame into spars contain 40 feet of olm 4 × 2½		10.	0.
,,	13 new short spars each 7 feet long long 3½ × 3.	1.	10.	6.
June 1st	Small curbb for petticoat		8.	0.

From this it is apparent that much of the old cap material was used more than once. The present cap is circular and is divided into twelve equal panels each in three parts vertically. The lower portion is divided into three by intermediate ribs, the middle section into two, and the upper is undivided. The new work is easily recognised.

			s.	d.
June 1st	2 cast iron plates for brake wheel. Wt. 3 cwt. 2 qrs. 20 lbs.	3.	0.	0.

These are to retain the folding wedges securing the brake wheel to the square on the wind shaft.

			s.	d.
June 1st	A new cast iron wind shaft Wt. 38 cwt. with neck and tail end turned up and a tail gudgeon turned up & bolted to same and an iron pullie bord out and bolted to pole end.	38.	0.	0.

This is the largest item and appears very reasonable since a pattern was required as well as a lot of machining involving a large lathe.

Next we have some items for the wind shaft bearings from which we learn that the neck brass weighed 31 lb., and the tail bearing 29½ lb.

			s.	d.
June 1st	2864 feet of weather board for cap	11.	18.	9.

This equals less than 8s. 6d. per square, a very low rate. The next items refer to the fittings for the fan gear. Among them we find such terms as: cog nuts, the 'hanging' of same, flyers, etc. The whole gear is described as 'wind tackle', a pinion is a 'spur nut', a plummer block is a 'chair'.

		£.	s.	d.
June 8th	2 fir midlings each 55 feet long 13 ins. square at centre.	18.	0.	0.

This is an extremely low figure. Mr. Clover in recent years has had to pay £70 for a single stock or middling. The size also is the largest we have met.

Next follow some items for parts of the winding gear, such as:— bevels, mitres, bracket chairs, etc. Then some pieces of fir and pitch pine 13 × 13 cross-section. These were for the supports of the upright shaft.

June 6th	A new cast iron end to fix on top of end of lower upright shaft turned up and duled (dowelled) and fitted and bolted to shaft 3 ft. long. Wt. 2 cwt. 3 qrs.	3.	0.	0.
,,	A new clutch bored out and turned up and fitted to same with one key. Wt. 1 cwt.	1.	12.	0.
,,	Turning up toe and flange of lower upright shaft.		18.	0.
,,	A new step brass for same bored out to fit. Wt. 30½ lbs.	2.	5.	9.
,,	Part of the upright shaft 8 ft. long Wt. 6 cwt. 2 qrs. 0 turned up at both ends and duled and turning both ends of old upright shaft and fitted to new parts and bolted together with 12 new bolts	8.	0.	0.

From the foregoing we gather that much of the old upright shaft was re-used with alterations and additions. It also gives us an idea of the cost of brass, viz. about 1s. 6d. per pound machined.

June ?	A piece of elm 5 ft. long 14 × 10 for neck block		16.	0.
,,	A cast iron bevell mortice wheel geared with wood cogs pitched and trimd for driving sack tackell	3.	10.	0
,,	A cast iron bevell cog nut to work in same pitched and trimd and fixed to a new 1¾ in. square turned up.	2.	12.	0.

Appendix C

These wheels are fixed just under the fifth floor, the large wheel being hung to the upright shaft. Note the millwright's terms: 'pitched and trimmed'.

	£.	s.	d.
June 11th Paid Sawyers for cutting 1340 of sawing in girders		2. 7.	0.

Considering that it is practically certain that all this work was done by hand over a pit the charge seems very reasonable. The next items cover small pieces of wood, nails and many rose nails for the cap. One of these items reads:

July 28th 1000 . 6d. and 500–8d. clasp nails	5. 0.

Nails in this account are consistantly referred to as: 2d, 3d, etc. These have no connection with money and this description can be traced back to Norman times. The scale runs:

$$2d. = 1 \text{ inch}$$
$$3d. = 1\tfrac{1}{4} \quad ,,$$
$$6d. = 2 \quad ,,$$
$$8d. = 2\tfrac{1}{2} \quad ,,$$
$$10d. = 3 \quad ,,$$

Then follow more items devoted to nails, floor brads, nut-headed screws, etc.

Sept. 8th 56 lbs. of hoop iron for floors	9. 0.

The use of hoop iron in place of wood tongues for the grooved flooring was common practice.

Sept 10th A cast iron spur wheel 6 ft. 2 in. diameter turnd up with iron cogs pitched and trimd and mortice bevell wheel on same geared with 96 wood cogs pitched and trimd 2 t. 13 cwt.	32. 0. 0.

This is the great spur wheel gearing with the stone nuts. At the time this mill was built there was not the same confidence among working millers as to the reliability of all-metal gear wheels. We are given to understand that in this instance the millwright only put it in under protest; in fact he was so dubious about the feasibility of the whole casting of this size that he induced Mr. Clover to purchase the pattern in case a replacement became necessary. This pattern was still in existence when the mill was dismantled and in excellent condition. It is also interesting to note that its services were never called upon.

			£	s.	d.
Aug. 10th	4 cast iron mortice stone nuts geared with wood cogs turnd up and pitched and trimd bored out and fitted to to 4 new stone spindles.		26.	0.	0.
„ 14th	4 bredgrass boxes fitted up with set screws.		2.	16.	0.

The expression 'bredgrass' is unusual. The term refers to the square box containing the footstep bearing of the quant or stone spindle and known as a bridging box.

Next we have sundry items for brasses, collars, etc., and then:

Aug. 14th	4 sets of ballance irons	4.	0.	0.

These obviously mean the governors or regulators.

Aug. 14th	4 sets of liter irons for stones consisting of liter beams and keeps 4 standards and fork beams and eyes screws and handles	4.	12.	0.

All this material will be easily recognised. Note the phonetic way of spelling the word 'liter'.

Then follow a number of items for small details including:—gear for raising the stone nuts out of gear, screws, brasses, chairs, spindles, etc. Among these we have a reference to the flour mill which was a large one and driven from the spur wheel by a bevel wheel bolted to the under face.

Aug. 21st	6 uplongs each 33½ feet long 1½ square	5.	0.

The uplong is the vertical outside edge of the sail frame and on to which the pivot bearing of the vanes are fixed. In this mill four uplongs are necessary for each sail frame as each carries two rows of vanes, fifteen pence seems cheap for an uplong of this length. By this time apparently the greater part of the heavy work was complete and the roof on and consequently most items now are for small things as nails, '2 gross' bolts, brais, hoop iron, etc. At this time also they were evidently taking in hand the sails.

Appendix C

			£.	s.	d.
Sept. 4th	12 sail bars 8½ ft. long.			15.	0.
,, ,,	64 feet of weather board to alter drift of sails			8.	0.

It will be seen that the sails here were very large. The use of weatherboards is interesting. The taper boarding was placed between the stock or middling and the whip so as to alter the angle of inclination of the sail to the wind. The use of weatherboard in this manner can be made to increase or decrease the drift at will.

			s.	d.
Sept. 8th	3 lbs. of sail nails.		1.	6.

These are short flat-headed nails for securing the canvas to the sail vanes.

		£.	s.	d.
Sept. 11th	6 new fins for wind tackell.	2.	8.	0.

We take this to mean blades for the wind vane or fan.

			s.	d.
Sept. 11th	A new triangle for sails.		4.	0.

This is the bell crank lever for giving motion from the cross on the end of the clothing rod to the shutter rod on the sail frame.

For about a month the men were engaged on small detail work in the interior and we get only small items for screws, stout screws, 1d. and 2d. nails, spindles, etc.

		£.	s.	d.
Oct. 11th	A new set of round vatts with bearers hopper and shoe.	3.	10.	0.
	2 new sets of round vatts for 4 ft. 6 in stones and iron stands for same.	5.	0.	0.

Vats are the portable wood casings surrounding the stones. For ease and cheapness of manufacture they are mostly octagonal but the round variety are probably the better. The iron stands are the frameworks for carrying the hopper, shoe, damsel support and in some cases the alarm bells.

			s.	d.
Oct. 11th	A new sack tackell roul 4 ft. 8 ins. long 7 in. diameter with gudgeons and hoops turned up.		16.	0.
,, ,,	1 pair chairs and brasses and 1 cupling brass for do.		13.	0.
,, ,,	A new rigour 19 in. diameter 6 in. thick fitted on sack tackell roul.		12.	0.

Appendix C

These items refer to the sack tackle. Some of the spelling is quaint. 'Rigour' is the double-flanged pulley for taking the slack belt for the drive.

Next some small items for the outer gallery, spindle alterations, nails, screws, etc. From now to the finish all the items are small but they contain some curious terms and a weird collection of materials.

		£.	s.	d.
Oct. 27th	54 feet of best hoisting chains for sack tackell 44 lbs.	1.	2.	0.
,, ,,	2 feeding jacks and plates (what are these?).		2.	6.
,, 29th	A new meal trough 8 feet long 3½ ft. deep in partition.	2.	12.	0.
Nov. 3rd	An iron screw graffil in 4 parts in under part of spur wheel.		3.	6.

This is a very obscure term. They are the four clamps securing the bevel for flour machine to the spur wheel.

		£.	s.	d.
Nov. 3rd	A cast iron swing frame and spindle and brasses etc. and a double wood rigour fixed to same.	1.	14.	0.

Probably for a jumper or reciprocating screen.

		£.	s.	d.
Nov. 3rd	A new stone box		12.	0.
Nov. 6th	Purches (purchase) rigour and shaft 3 ft. long.		6.	0.
,, ,,	A peace of leather for flour mill.		5.	0.
,, ,,	A peace of do 5 ft. long 1½ in. wide for sack tackell		3.	0.
Nov. 9th	A new shoe for vatts		4.	6.
Nov. 12th	3 new corn screens each 8 ft. long 14 in. wide.	2.	10.	0.
Nov. 20th	2000 clasp nails 'sartid'.		5.	6.
,, ,,	Pait 'tea' joints.		1.	0.
Dec. 4th	3 cast blocks for ballancing sails Wt. 1 cwt. 0 0.		12.	0.

This clearly demonstrates the necessity for careful balancing the rotating system even for such slow rates of revolution as a windmill sail.

		£.	s.	d.
Dec. 18th	18 lbs. sheet 'zink'.		4.	6.
Jan. 21st	Use of crabb.		15.	0.
	This works out at 6d. per week.			
,, ,,	Workmanship frameing curbb = sheer trees and cap at Sudbury.	7.	10.	0.

Appendix C

The sum total for all the material supplied by Bear was £353 6s. 9d.

It is apparent that much material was re-used from the old mill, e.g. there is no mention of stones of which this mill had five pairs. Brickwork is not included, nor doors, etc. Ladders do not appear nor weighing machines, flour machine, galleries nor sails and clothing tackle. It is evident therefore that a mill of this magnitude was even in those days a very expensive proposition.

The Buxhall labour bill although of not the same interest as that for the materials is still worth some consideration. The bill is made out weekly and contains a list of the men engaged and their totals for the week. Actually sixteen men were in all employed, their names being: Brand (a boy), Pratt, H. R. Rayner, Chinery, Cole, Starrs, H. Turner, Mason, E. Adams, Wollard, Peck, Robson, Clark, G. Rayner, Harper and Catchpole. Of these Wollard, Pratt, Chinery, Robson and Clark were employed only occasionally, from which we must conclude that they were specialists and were only called upon to carry out their own particular jobs; one must have been expert in pitching and trimming cogs, and other jobs will occur to the millwright. The bulk of the work was done by the remainder and their daily wages varied from 1s. to 4s. 8d., the actual rates being:

Brand (a boy)	1s.	per day	E. Adams	3s.	per day (3s. 6d. later)
Pratt	1s. 4½d.	,, ,,	Wollard	3s.	,, ,,
H. Rayner	2s. 6d.	,, ,,	G. Rayner	3s. 6d.	,, ,,
Chinery	2s. 6d.	,, ,,	Harper	3s. 6d.	,, ,,
Cole	3s.	,, ,,	Robson	4s.	,, ,,
Starrs	3s.	,, ,,	Clark	4s.	,, ,,
H. Turner	3s.	,, ,,	Peck	4s. 6d.	,, ,,
Mason	3s.	,, ,,	Catchpole	4s. 6d.	,, ,,

The men started on 5th May, 1860, and the last man left on 2nd February in the following year, and the rates of pay remained stationary throughout this time with the sole exception of E. Adams who managed a rise of 6d. per day during the course of the work.

The number of days per week worked by the men varied but there are some entries of 7 days per week per man and in some cases 7½ days per week. These excessive rates prevail only in the height of the summer months, June and July. To those who know the Clover family it is difficult to believe that they would permit Sunday labour so we are of the opinion that a bonus was paid for working all weekday hours possible.

Appendix C

However, business did not come to a standstill as in the fifties. Mr. Clover built a steam mill and installed an old-type beam steam engine driving two pairs of stones and a flour bolting machine. This gave him a decided advantage over his neighbours, who were dependent on the summer wind and water. His son put in a larger boiler and an extra pair of stones with a purifier and a centrifugal and other dressing machines; the consequence was that the extra strain broke the beam and wrecked the whole engine, and although he had it built up again it never worked well. To revert to the contract, the highest paid men were Peck and Catchpole, who by putting in a full week of 6 days could earn the not very large sum of 27s. 6d. per week. Most probably Bob Catchpole was in charge and he was the inventor (although the idea originated with Mr. Clover) of the auxiliary shutters found here and elsewhere in this district where they are described as sky-scrapers. They were fitted to the tower mill at Rattlesden near by. They comprise a few additional shutters set longitudinally and worked by the same shutter rods as the main shutters. In fair winds they give additional sail area but in high winds the least tilt of the shutters causes them to act as a brake, and a very effective one which when fully open brought Buxhall Mill to a complete standstill, without the use of the normal brake but solely by the action of Catchpole's patent auxiliary shutters.

We give two specimen weeks' entries:

				£.	s.	d.
July 28th	3½ days work		Peck		15.	9.
,,	7	,, ,,	Catchpole	1.	11.	6.
,,	6	,, ,,	Starrs		18.	0.
,,	6½	,, ,,	Rayner		16.	3.
,,	7	,, ,,	Mason	1.	4.	6.
,,	6	,, ,,	Brand		6.	0.
,,	7	,, ,,	Cole	1.	1.	0.
Oct. 6th	7	,, ,,	Catchpole	1.	11.	6.
,,	7	,, ,,	Mason	1.	4.	6.
,,	7	,, ,,	H. Rayner	1.	17.	6.
,,	1	,, ,,	Chinery		2.	6.
,,	4½	,, ,,	Cole		13.	6.
,,	5	,, ,,	Brand		5.	0.
,,	3½	,, ,,	Peck		15.	6.
,,	1	,, ,,	Robson		4.	0.

The last item in the wages bill is:

Paid for mens lodgings   5. 14. 0.

Appendix C

It is difficult to see how this small sum could serve for such a large number of men-weeks. There were no such things as cycles in those days and it is a long way from Buxhall to Sudbury. Probably some accommodation may have been found for the men on the site. The sum total according to Bear's reckoning was £152 18s. 6d. We have carefully checked his addition and the actual amount should have been £152 8s. 8d., so that on this occasion Mr. Clover was overcharged by 9s. 10d.

Buxhall Mill is a large tower of brick with six floors. It had a stage, four sails (patent), and five pairs of stones, oat crusher and two flour machines. It contained also a grain-cleaner, sack tackle and the usual equipment of an up-to-date mill. The tower is built on the foundations of the 1815 mill; these are a yard wide but only go into the ground about a foot. The authorities tried to stop Mr. Clover from building so near the house but they could not prevent him from using the old foundations; the site is a very stiff blue clay and has stood the strain of the increased weight. The mill was fitted later with electric light and was always admirably maintained by its owner Mr. J. A. Clover, grandson of the builder. We have this gentleman's permission to quote extracts from these almost unique documents and also have to thank him for various visits and for much useful information. Unfortunately the mill was much damaged in a gale in 1929 and it was found necessary to remove the sails and fly tackle so that all milling has now to be done by oil power.

The Clover family are very old-established in Suffolk and Essex; in fact their connection can be traced back for more than three hundred years and branches of the family are still working in the corn trade.

APPENDIX D

STONE DRESSING[1]

BY MR. JOHN RUSSELL

THE tools needed for stone dressing are simple and may be divided into two groups—those for test and those for cutting. Tools for test comprise the iron proof staff, wooden paint staff and furrowing strips.

Cutting tools comprise mill bills and the thrift for holding them.

The proof staff is a long narrow cast-iron surface plate mounted in a wooden case with a hinged cover. The usual size is about four feet wide and its purpose is to test the accuracy of the wooden paint staff. Every time the miller dresses a pair of stones he proves the staff. A small quantity of oil is applied to the proof and the staff lightly rubbed upon it, the high places being marked with oil; these are reduced by scraping—either a steel scraper or a piece of glass being used, generally the latter. Alternate rubbing and scraping is continued until the staff shows even marking throughout its entire length. The staff—about four feet long by three inches wide by five inches deep—is sometimes made of red deal or oak and sometimes of mahogany or walnut. The best is made by sawing timber longitudinally into three pieces, the two outer strips reversed in position and jointed with glue and brass screws. Staffs so made are less inclined to warp with changing weather conditions than staffs of one piece. A rubbing burr is used to smooth the surface of millstones before applying the staff, especially after any facing (or flawing as it is often called); it is merely a small burr with one side faced to a flat surface.

The furrowing strips, made from red deal or pine, about three-eighths inch in thickness, are two in number, one the width of the

[1] Reproduced by permission from his paper, ' Mill Stones in Wind and Water Mills', *Transactions of the Newcomen Society*, Vol. XXIV, 1944.

furrow and one the width of the 'land', i.e. the surface of stone lying between furrows, the length being rather greater than the distance from the eye to the edge of the stone (Fig. 64).

Mill bills are made of best quality high carbon steel and when new are about eleven inches in length, one-and-a-half inch square in the middle and drawn out to a chisel point at each end with the cutting facets ground to about forty degrees. The weight, from three to three-and-a-half pounds when new, with repeated grinding and forging is gradually reduced; when less than two pounds they are generally considered too light for further use. In the mills where peak stones were run, old flat mill bills were often beaten into picks for stitching, for which purpose they can be used until about one pound in weight. The miller needs a good grindstone and a stone to set his bills upon. Too much rubbing is to be deprecated, there being a temptation to make the edge too obtuse. The thrift for holding mill bills is generally made from ash, sometimes from chestnut or beech. The mortises in wooden thrifts are often fitted with a hardwood tongue with a rounded back as this accommodates itself to variations in the mill bill taper holding it more securely.

French millstones run about twelve days between dressing. When a pair is taken up for this purpose the runner is laid in any convenient place, often on a wooden turntable; this is a great advantage enabling that portion of the stone worked upon to be brought into a good light. The bed stone must be dressed *in situ*. When the stones are ready for dressing, the miller first rubs the face of each stone with the burr; this removes any possibility of scratching the staff and causes the stone to show the tiver marks more clearly.

The next operation is staffing. A little tiver, made from red iron oxide, is mixed with water and applied to the face of the staff. It is usual to employ two brushes for this purpose, one wet and one dry. By using the wet brush first the staff is well covered; superfluous tiver is removed by dry brushing. After the tiver is laid on, the staff is placed upon each stone and rotated over the whole of the surface; a fresh application of tiver is needed for each stone. If the stones are in good trim the tiver from the staff will be evenly distributed on the stone face from the periphery to about halfway to the eye.

The stones are now ready for cracking. Millers divide the surface of the stone into three zones, the first from the circumference called the skirt about one-third of the radius, the second the breast, and that near the centre the eye. It is usual to put in about sixteen cracks per inch of uniform depth at the skirt, becoming lighter to die out finally about the middle of the breast. Anywhere marked by tiver is cracked; places unmarked are not touched. Much is heard about neat cracking, but of equal importance is keeping the face straight—burrs, in spite of careful selection, vary much in texture and hardness. Where the stone is at all soft, great care must be exercised in cracking—there is always a tendency to get the cracks too deep where the going is good; if this is done the next time the stones come up, these places will have worn more than the harder parts and will be below the staff. The miller must let them severely alone until such time as they come up again. From the middle of the breast to the eye of the stone should be as smooth as possible and below the staff, generally enough to draw a piece of writing paper about four inches from the eye. When stones are taken up for re-dressing the cracks are not worn completely out; the stones are dull because the edges of the cracks have lost their sharpness. Recracking takes place in the original marks; in the course of time this makes the cracks too wide and when this stage is reached it is usual to cross the work, i.e. crack the lands diagonally, for a few dresses until such times as the old cracks are obliterated. New cracks are then put in. It is not necessary to touch the eye burrs every dress; when they show signs of getting up as the millers say, they must be flawed. Sometimes a short staff, the eye staff, about half the stone's diameter, is used to show the high places which are taken down with a sharp bill crossing the work after each staffing followed by a good rubbing.

If the face of a stone becomes crooked the bran will be curled and cut, spoiling the colour of the flour. If the stones are in good condition the wheat berry is opened out by the eye burrs, the kernel gradually reduced in the breast, the skirt completing the operation, and scraping and cleaning the bran. The condition of the bran is the best index of the standard of the stone dressing and should be in large flakes, thin, flat and clean.

Furrowing is to some extent an occasional job, sometimes one or two quarters are done per dress, while some millers do not touch them for a number of dresses and then refurrow the whole at one time. The furrows are marked with the furrowing strips, the first laid in the master furrow, the second immediately behind it on the land. After the master furrow is marked the strip is transferred to the next

furrow, being held closely to the land strip, moving the strips alternately until a quarter is marked. A feather suitably trimmed is
dipped in tiver and drawn along the edge of each strip as they are
moved from furrow to furrow, leaving a thin red line for the miller
to work to.

Mill bills must be very hard to cut French burrs; small particles fly
from them from time to time and some of these pieces imbed themselves in the back of the stone-dresser's left hand, especially in the
case of those with tender skins; some millers' hands were quite
blackened. When every village possessed a wind- or watermill there
was always a number of men who tramped the country seeking for
the job of stone dressing; some merely cadgers, some genuinely want-
ing work. If a miller needed help the man who could 'show his steel'
was more likely to be allowed to 'show his metal' than one who could
not. Windmillers who had work to offer were in the habit of adver-
tising the fact with their sweeps, setting the bottom one just in
advance of the vertical; any strolling stone-dresser noting a sweep in
this position knew that a job was available.

Where two men are employed, it is the privilege of the senior to
dress the runner, upon which he sits sideways, his body inclined forward, elbows resting on a small cushion of bran, the bist, the
extremity of the thrift grasped in his right hand, his left near its
head. Meanwhile his less fortunate colleague lies either upon his
left side, or kneels if the bed stone is adjacent to either stones or
machinery.

For grinding oats and other corn for feed, before the introduction
of artificial stones, Peak stones from Derbyshire were in general use.
In this case the miller aims at cutting up as much of the outer husk
as possible and the dress was modified accordingly, twice the draft
of a french stone is the common rule, the usual allowance being one
inch draft per foot, that is to say, the fore-edge of the master furrow in
a peak stone four feet in diameter is tangential to a circle eight inches
in diameter; for a french stone of the same size it is tangential to a
circle four inches in diameter. Where comparatively rough grinding
was done it was usual to employ a greater number of quarters and
deeper furrows for fine grinding, the lands being coarsely cracked
about four per inch.

In Sussex, where fine grinding of oats for poultry feeding became
quite an industry, a finer dress was called for; the stones—usually

four feet in diameter (smaller were considered inadvisable)—were set out with ten quarters of four furrows broad and shallow, or as the millers said, 'broad and fleet'—the land being pitted with a number of fine holes made with a sharp pointed bill known as a pick. The miller was careful to stagger the stitching as this operation was called, making it deepest at the skirt, dying out in the breast.

Both runner and bed stones were kept well hollowed from breast to eye to give them what the millers called swallow, the stone near the eye being about a quarter inch below the staff; if this is not done, uneven feeding known as gorging results.

Peak stones used for oat-grinding needed much power and soon became dull, wearing much faster than stones used for flour making. It was usual to face the stones every dress as they invariably wore into rings; generally the staff was applied only once, the high places being reduced with a sharp bill; occasionally a second facing was required. After facing, all furrows were deepened, this being necessary every dress. The final operation of stitching made the stones ready for another spell of work.

Where oats are still ground by stones, the composition kind holds the field, the output being three times that of peak stone and the dress lasting three times as long. The circular or sickle dress is often employed with artificial stones. If plenty of power is available, stones grind faster with sickle furrows; composition stones have a naturally rough face and need no stitching or cracking, in itself a great economy.

Mill Bills.—When the miller found his bills unduly thick or getting soft he sent them to the local forge. Before taking a long heat on the end he intended to forge first, the smith drew the temper of the opposite end; unless that was done cracking followed the first blows of the hammer. The preliminary drawing was done on the anvil bick finishing on the face, care being taken to avoid striking the bills edgeways when at all cooled; light blows with a small hammer, continued until the red had almost faded, were supposed to impart toughness. Several heats were necessary on each end before the bills were thin enough, some practice being necessary to keep them square and straight without winding. Hardening in a charcoal fire was always done after dark; the smith had no pyrometer or other refinements, having to judge the heat entirely by colour; the dark cherry red heat necessary could be easily exceeded in daylight. The bills were heated about one and a half to two inches back, first quenched in pickle, finally cooled in water. After the hardening of the second end the bills were completely submerged until quite cool, the temper not drawn in any way—the hardened portion showed a light grey colour hard enough to scratch glass; if softer than this they would not cut french burr. Thin fresh-forged mill bills were kept for cracking and facing; when too thick and clumsy for this purpose they were suitable for furrowing. Mill picks were drawn down by the smith to about one-eighth inch square, the miller grinding them to a point, some making them round, the more precise square. In grinding, the bill is held against a rest fixed to the grindstone frame, (the stone running towards the operator) resulting in quicker sharpening with less fatigue than holding in the unsupported hands.

FIG. 64. STONES AND TACKLE: UNION MILL, CRANBROOK

Glossary

AIR POLES, connect the shutter bars of roller reefing sails with the spider.

ANNULAR SAIL, has a single row of shutters in a circle.

BACKSTAYS, wooden stays at the back which serve to maintain the weather of the sail.

BALANCE DISH, automatic grain feed to the hopper.

BAR, lateral member of a sail frame.

BAY, gap between the bars of shuttered sails.

BED STONE, the lower or nether mill stone.

BELL ALARM, contrivance to give warning when grain runs low in the hopper.

BILL, chisel used for dressing stones.

BIN, storage for grain.

BIN FLOOR, upper floor where the bins are located.

BIST, cushion of bran for the elbows when stone dressing.

BLUE STONE, imported from Germany, syn. cullin stone.

BODY (of a post mill), contains the machinery.

BOLTER, machine for dressing flour out of meal.

BOLTING CLOTH, woollen cloth for bolter.

BRAKE, contracts on the brake wheel to stop the mill.

BRAKE LEVER, pivoted beam used to apply the brake.

BRAKE ROPE, control for the brake lever.

BRAKE WHEEL, mounted on the windshaft and driving the wallower. On its rim the brake acts.

BRAY, intermediate lever connecting the bridge tree and steelyard.

BREAST (of post mill), forward end, just behind the sails.

BREAST (of stones), middle third of the grinding face.

BREAST BEAM, main beam in the breast taking the weight of the windshaft, syn. rode balk, weather beam.

BREAST CAP SILLS, two timbers used to support the roof members of some caps.

BRIDGE TREE, hinged beam supporting a stone spindle.

BRIDGING BOX, adjustable housing for a thrust bearing.

BRIDLE IRONS, clamps to hold a sail back to the arm of a cross.

BROAD AND FLEET, broad and shallow furrows in a mill stone.

BUCK, body of a post mill (Suffolk).

BURR STONE, imported from France, syn. french burr.

CANT, part of the framing of a wooden gear wheel on which the rim is fixed.

213

Glossary

CANT POSTS, corner posts of a smock mill.

CAP, movable top of a tower or smock mill.

CAP CIRCLE, sub-frame from which spring the rafters of some caps.

CAP FRAME, main base frame of a cap.

CAP PIECE, rear tie beam of the sheers.

CAP SPARS, rafters of the cap.

CASING (for stones), wooden case enclosing a pair of stones, syn. vat, tun.

CENTRE BEAM, beam in the centre of the cap frame.

CHAIN PURCHASE WHEEL (Suffolk), see Y-wheel.

CLAMPS, strengthening timbers for the stock or middling.

CLASP ARM WHEEL, construction of a wooden gear wheel of which the arms clasp the shaft and one another, cf. compass arm.

CLOTH SAILS, spread with sail cloths, syn. common sails.

CLOTHING, act of spreading cloths or closing shutters of sails.

CLOTHS, are spread on the sails.

COCK HEAD, top of the stone spindle.

COLLAR, steady bearing round the post in the bottom floor of a post mill body.

COLLAR (of a tail pole), see yoke.

COMMON SAILS, are spread with sail cloths, syn. cloth sails.

COMPASS ARM WHEEL, wooden gear wheel with arms mortised through a wooden shaft, cf. clasp arm.

COMPOSITE MILL, a post mill body taken off its post and mounted on a short tower.

COMPOSITION STONES, made up from cement and carborundum or other abrasive.

COUNTER BACKS, special clamps behind the sails in use in the north-west.

COW-POP GEAR, has pegs instead of cogs, syn. trundle wheel.

CRACKING, CRACKS, the fine lines or grooves cut in the lands of a dressed mill stone.

CROSS, multi-armed casting mounted on the end of a windshaft to carry sails on its arms.

CROSSTREES, main horizontal beams of the substructure of a post mill.

CROTCH (of a quant), forked lower end of a quant which engages with the mace or rynd.

CROTCH SPINDLE (Suffolk), see quant.

CROWNTREE, horizontal beam, which bears on top of the post of a post mill.

CULLIN STONES, imported from Cologne, syn. blue stones.

CURB, track on top of the tower of a mill on which the cap turns, cf. dead curb and live curb,

DAGGER POINT, second of four positions for spreading a sail cloth.

DAMSEL, iron forging agitating the shoe of underdrift stones.

DEAD CURB, has a rubbing contact only with bearing blocks on the cap frame.

Glossary

DEAD LEAD, boarding in place of some of the shutters in the leading edge of a sail.

DOUBLE SHUTTERED, sail with shutters on both leading and trailing sides of the whip.

DRAFT, position of the furrows on a stone.

DRESSING (of meal), separating the flour from the rest of the meal.

DRESSING (of stones), sharpening stones (generally speaking).

DRIVING SIDE, trailing side of a sail.

DUST FLOOR, top floor of tower mill.

EYE (of a stone), (a) hole in the centre of the runner stone, (b) inner third of the grinding surface.

EYE (of the wind), square into the wind.

EYE STAFF, short staff used for proving the eye of the stone (b above).

FAN BRACES, brace the fan spars.

FAN SPARS, wooden uprights supporting the fan, syn. fly posts.

FAN STAGE, below the fantail of a tower mill.

FANTAIL, turns the mill into the wind automatically, syn. fly.

FIRST REEF, third of four positions for spreading a sail cloth.

FLOATS, paddles of the scoop wheel of a drainage mill.

FLY, FLYPOSTS, see fantail, fan spars.

FRENCH STONE, built up of blocks of a freshwater quartz, syn. burr stone.

FULL SAIL, last of four positions for spreading a sail cloth.

FURROWING STRIPS, used for marking out the furrows on a millstone.

FURROWS, channels cut in the grinding face of a millstone.

GALLERY, platform round the cap of a tower mill.

GATE, slide controlling the flow of grain from the shoe to the stones.

GETTING UP (a french stone), the wearing of the eye burrs.

GIRTS, timbers running the full length of the side of a post mill, syn. side girts or summers.

GLUTBOX, used for throwing a stone nut on a quant out of gear.

GORGING, uneven feeding of grain through the stones.

GOVERNOR, automatic device to (a) maintain the gap between the stones, (b) regulate the speed of a machine.

GRAFT SHAFT, upright shaft with sections of both iron and wood.

GREASE WEDGE, removable portion of the bearing round the neck of a stone spindle.

GREAT SPUR WHEEL, mounted on the upright shaft and driving the stone nuts.

GREY STONES, of millstone grit, syn. peak stones.

GRIPE, syn. for brake (Norfolk).

GRIPED ARM, syn. for clasp arm (Norfolk).

GRIST, (a) corn to be ground, (b) animal feed.

GROAT MACHINE, used for separating the husk from groats.

GUDGEON, iron journal attached to a wooden shaft.

HACKLE PLATE, with a leather washer it keeps dirt from entering the neck bearing of the stone spindle.

Glossary

HEAD SICK, said of a post mill with the body canted forward.

HEAD WHEEL, syn. brake wheel.

HEMLATH, longitudinal member at the edge of a sail frame, syn. outside rule.

HOLLOW POST MILL, has drive by an upright shaft taken down through the centre of the post to machinery below.

HOPPER, container for grain mounted above and feeding the stones.

HORIZONTAL MILL, has sails revolving in a horizontal plane on a vertical shaft.

HORSE, framework on top of the stone casings supporting the hopper and shoe.

HURST, framework on which underdrift stones are mounted when the drive is on the same floor.

HUSK CUPBOARD, container for oat husks winnowed out of a groat machine.

INTO HOUSE, the operation of pulling the sails closer to the body of the mill.

JACK, tool used in setting the stone spindle vertical.

JIB SAILS, triangular sail cloths wound round a radial sail arm with the tip of the sail corded to the next arm.

JOG-SCRY, an inclined oscillating sieve.

JUMPER, syn. jog-scry.

KEEP FLANGE, on the inner side of the curb under which the truck wheels run.

KEST, toll cupboard (Anglesey).

LANDS, grinding areas of a millstone.

LANTERN PINION, gear having staves between two flanges instead of cogs.

LATHS, longitudinal members of a sail frame.

LEADING BOARD, narrow board fixed to the leading edge of both common and single shuttered sails.

LIGHTER SCREW, passes through the bridge tree and is used to raise or lower it.

LISTINGS, webbing straps connecting the blinds of roller reefing sails.

LIVE CURB, on which rollers run.

MACE, a part of the drive to the stones.

MANYHEIGHT, stepped pivot for a crowbar, used when raising a runner stone.

MEAL BIN, receives the meal from the stones.

MEAL FLOOR, below the stone floor.

MEAL MAN, separated the flour from the bran until wind-driven bolters were in use, after which the miller became the meal man.

MEAL SPOUT, conveys the meal from the stones to the meal bins or bags.

MIDDLING, timber to which two sails are fixed (Kent), syn. stock.

NECK (of stone spindle), upper journal.

NECK (of windshaft), front journal.

NECK BEARING, front bearing of a wind shaft, syn. neck brass.

NECK STUDS, vertical timbers holding the neck bearing assembly in place.

Glossary

OUT OF HOUSE, the operation of pushing the sails away from the body of the mill.

OUTSIDE RULE, longitudinal member at the edge of a sail frame, syn. hemlath.

OVERDRIFT, stones driven from above.

PAINT STAFF, of wood used for marking high spots when stone dressing.

PATENT SAIL, shuttered self-regulating sail.

PEAK STONE, of millstone grit, syn. grey stone.

PETTICOAT, downward extension of the weatherboarding of a post mill body or a tower mill cap.

PICK, pointed mill bill for dressing stones.

PIERS, of brick, supporting the ends of the crosstrees of a post mill.

PINTLE, small diameter journal projecting from (a) a wooden shaft, (b) the top of a post.

PIT WHEEL, driven gear mounted on the scoop wheel shaft.

POINTING LINES, cords attached to sail cloths and used when clothing a common sail.

POLL END, POLL, cast-iron socket end of a windshaft in which the stocks (or middlings) are held, syn. cannister.

POST, upright timber on top of which the body of a post mill turns.

POST MILL, one having a body mounted and turning on an upright post.

PROOF STAFF, of iron, for proving the working face of the paint staff when dressing stones.

PUNCHEONS, horizontal timbers bracing the cap circle to the sheers.

QUANT, spindle carrying the stone nut driving an overdrift stone.

QUARTER (of a smock mill), one of the sides of a smock mill.

QUARTERBARS, diagonal timbers of the substructure of a post mill.

QUARTERING, turning the sails at ninety degrees to the direction of the wind.

RACK, gearing round the curb on top of a mill tower.

RADDLE, red oxide and water or fat used on the paint staff when dressing stones, syn. tiver.

RAP, block of hard wood or bone on the shoe to take the knock of the quant or damsel.

RIGGER, contrivance using chains or straps to lift a stone nut up out of gear with the great spur wheel.

RODE BALK, main beam in the breast taking the weight of the windshaft, syn. breast beam.

ROLLER REEFING SAILS, use roller blinds instead of shutters but are not automatic.

ROUNDHOUSE, (a) of a post mill encloses the substructure, (b) of a tower mill built round the outside of the lower floor or floors.

RUBBING BURR, piece of french burr used to rub down high spots when stone dressing.

RUNNER STONE, upper stone of a pair.

Glossary

RYND, let into the runner stone to take the drive before the mace and bar were introduced.

SACK CHAIN, lifting chain used for hoisting sacks.

SACK HOIST, mechanism for hoisting sacks.

SACK JIGGER, forked lever used to knock a suspended sack on the floor and shake down the contents.

SACK SLIDE, at the side of a post mill ladder for lowering sacks.

SAILS, for driving windmills, syn. sweeps (Kent).

SAIL BACK, backbone of a sail mounted on a cross.

SAIL BARS, transverse members of a sail frame.

SAIL IN, to close the shutters of a sail.

SAIL OUT, to open the shutters of a sail.

SAIL RODS, see shutter bars.

SAMSON HEAD, castings strengthening the top of the post and the bottom of the crowntree.

SCOOP WHEEL, with floats used for drainage.

SHEAVES, wheels fixed to the underside of the cap frame to centre the cap, syn. truck wheels, truckles.

SHEERS, two timbers extending from breast to tail, (a) of a cap, (b) below a post mill body.

SHOW HIS STEEL, to prove that he is an experienced stone dresser.

SHOE, inclined trough down which grain passes from the hopper to the stones.

SHOT CURB, live curb on which a ring of rollers runs.

SHUTTERS (of sails), hinged in a spring or patent sail, syn. shades, vanes.

SHUTTER BARS connect together all the shutters in one side of a sail, syn. sail rods.

SHUDES, unshelled oats.

SICKLE DRESS, stone dressing with curved furrows.

SIDE GIRTS (upper, lower), timbers running the full length of the sides of a post mill body.

SINGLE SHUTTERED, sail with shutters on the trailing side of the whip only.

SKIRT, outer third of the grinding surface of a stone.

SKY-SCRAPERS, air brakes, or spoilers, on sails (Suffolk).

SLIP COGS, removable cogs in a gear.

SMOCK MILL, tower mill with a wooden tower.

SMUTTER, machine to remove smut from grain.

SOKE (milling), feudal customs relating to manorial mills.

SPIDER, coupling fixed to the front end of the striking rod.

SPILL THE WIND, to open the shutters in a sail which is driving.

SPINDLEBEAM, carries the top bearing of the upright shaft in a post mill, syn. tie beam.

SPRATTLE BEAM, fixed horizontal beam carrying a vertical thrust bearing.

SPRING SAILS, shuttered sails with the shutters in each sail controlled by a spring.

Glossary

SPRING-PATENT SAILS, patent sails with springs incorporated in the striking gear.

SPURNS, fan stage members.

STAFF, of wood used for marking high spots when stone dressing, syn. paint staff.

STAGE, platform round the body of a mill.

STARTS, carry the floats of a scoop wheel.

STAVES, those parts of a lantern pinion, taking the part of cogs in a spur wheel.

STEELYARD, iron lever, the final one in the system connecting the bridge tree to the governors.

STITCHING, cutting the small grooves in the lands when stone dressing. Pits at irregular intervals instead of grooves are cut for grinding oats.

STOCK, timber to which two sails are fitted, syn. middling (Kent).

STONES, used for grinding grain.

STONE CASING, wooden casing enclosing the stones. syn. tun, vat.

STONE DRESSING, sharpening the stones.

STONE FLOOR, on which the stones are situated.

STONE NUT, final driven pinion in the drive to the stones.

STONE SPINDLE, on top of which the runner stone is balanced.

STORM HATCH, above the neck of the windshaft giving access to the sails.

STRIKING CHAIN, used for opening (a) the shutters in a patent sail, (b) the blinds in a roller reefing sail.

STRIKING GEAR (front and rear), collective meaning for the mechanism used to open and close (a) the shutters of a patent sail, (b) the blinds of a roller reefing sail.

STRIKING ROD, passes through the windshaft and connects the front and rear striking gear in patent or roller reefing sails.

STUMP IRONS, bolted to the stocks to support the triangles of the striking gear.

SUBSTRUCTURE, supports the body of a post mill.

SUNK POST MILL, has its substructure buried in the ground.

SWALLOW, relief of the grinding surface round the eye of the stone.

SWEEP, used for driving a mill (Kent), syn. sail.

SWING POT NECK, self-aligning neck bearing (East Anglia).

SWORD POINT, first of four positions for spreading a sail cloth.

TAIL (of a post mill), rear end.

TAIL BEAM, carries the tail bearing of the windshaft, syn. tailbalk.

TAIL BEARING (of windshaft), journal bearing at the rear of the windshaft.

TAIL BLOCK, used when the tailbeam is dispensed with.

TAIL POLE, lever for winding a mill by hand.

TAIL END TIE BEAM, carries the tail block when the tail beam is dispensed with.

TAIL WHEEL, mounted on the tail of the windshaft in a post mill.

TAIL-WINDING, when the wind catches the sails from the rear.

TEME, sieve used in bolting meal by hand.

Glossary

TENTERING, adjusting the distance between the stones.

THRIFT, wood handle into which mill bills or picks are wedged.

THRUST BLOCK, carries the thrust bearing of the windshaft.

TILLER, lever pivoted on the side of the tail pole and used to raise the ladder of a post mill off the ground.

TIVER, red oxide and fat or water used for finding high spots when stone dressing, syn. raddle.

TOLL, payment in kind for grinding corn or dressing meal.

TOLL CUPBOARD, to contain the above, syn. kest (Anglesey).

TOWER MILL, has tower of brick, masonry, or other material.

TRAIL STICK, lever actuating a bell alarm.

TRIANGLES, cranks used in the front striking gear of patent sails.

TRUCK WHEEL, TRUCKLE, runs against the inside face of the curb to centre the cap.

TRUNDLE WHEEL, gear having pegs instead of cogs, syn. cow-pop gear.

TWIST PEG, wooden peg operating the cord controlling the flow of grain from the shoe into the eye of the stone.

UNDERDRIFT, stones driven from below.

UPLONG, longitudinal member of a sail frame.

UPRIGHT SHAFT, on which the wallower and great spur wheel are mounted.

VANES, (a) of a sail, syn. shades, shutters; (b) of a fantail, syn. blades.

VAT, wooden case enclosing a pair of stones, syn. casing, tun.

WALLOWER, the first driven wheel in a mill with indirect drive to the stones, syn. wallow-wheel.

WEATHER, the twist in a sail to give driving power.

WEATHER-BEAM, main beam in the breast taking the weight of the windshaft, syn. breast beam, rode balk.

WELL FRAME, suspended from the cap frame and used to centre the cap (north-west).

WHIP, backbone of a sail attached to a stock or middling.

WINDING, turning the mill so that the sails face square into the wind.

WINDSHAFT, carries the sails and the brake wheel.

WIRE MACHINE, used to separate flour out of the meal in several qualities instead of one, cf. bolter.

Y-WHEEL, has forks like Ys round the circumference to carry a chain or rope.

YOKE, two wooden bars fixed to the tail pole to push against when winding a post mill, syn. collar.

Bibliography[1]

BATTEN, M. I., *English Windmills*, Vol. I. Containing a history of their origin and development, with records of mills in Kent, Surrey and Sussex (Architectural Press, 1930).

BENNETT, RICHARD, and ELTON, JOHN, *History of Corn Milling*. Vol. I. Handstones, Slave and Cattle Mills, 1898; Vol. II. Watermills and Windmills, 1899; Vol. III. Feudal Laws and Customs, 1900; Vol. IV. Some Feudal Mills, 1904 (Simpkin Marshall).

BRANGWYN, FRANK, and PRESTON, HAYTER, *Windmills* (John Lane, 1923).

CLARK, ALLEN, *Windmill Land*. Rambles in Old-fashioned Lancashire Countryside, with Chat about its History and Romance (W. Foulsham, 1932).

DARBY, H. C., *The Draining of the Fens* (Cambridge University Press, Cambridge, 1940).

DOUCH, H. H., *Cornish Windmills* (Oscar Blackford, Truro, n.d.).

FARRIES, K. G., and MASON, M. T., *The Windmills of Surrey and Inner London* (Charles Skilton, London, 1966).

FINCH, WILLIAM COLES, *Watermills and Windmills*. A Historical Survey of their Rise, Decline and Fall as Portrayed by those of Kent (C. W. Daniel, 1933).

FOWELL, G. M., and HUGHES, A. FOORD, *Windmills in Sussex*. Being Nos. 29–30 of Walker's *Quarterly* (Walker's Galleries).

FREESE, STANLEY, *Windmills and Millwrighting* (Cambridge University Press, 1957).

HARRISON, H. C., *The Story of Sprowston Mill* (Phoenix House, 1949).

HEMMING, PETER, *Windmills in Sussex*. A description of the Construction and Operation of Windmills, exemplified by Up-to-Date Notes on the still existing Windmills in Sussex with photographic illustrations (C. W. Daniel, 1936).

HENNELL, THOMAS, *The Countryman at Work* (Architectural Press, 1947).

HOPKINS, R. THURSTON, *Old English Mills and Inns* (Cecil Palmer, 1927).

HOPKINS R. THURSTON, *Old Watermills and Windmills* (Philip Allen, n.d.).

HOPKINS, R. THURSTON, and FREESE, STANLEY, *In Search of English Windmills* (Cecil Palmer, 1931).

[1] All published in London unless otherwise noted.

Bibliography

SAUNDERS, JAMES EDWIN, *The Reflections and Rhymes of an Old Miller* (Hodder & Stoughton, n.d.).

SKILTON, C. P., *British Windmills and Watermills* (Collins, 1947).

SMEATON, JOHN, *An Experimental Enquiry concerning the Natural Powers of Water and Wind to turn Mills and other Machines, depending on a Circular Motion* (I. &. J. Taylor, 1794).

SMEATON, JOHN, Reports of the late John Smeaton, F.R.S., made on Various Occasions in the Course of his Employment as a Civil Engineer, 3 volumes (Longman, Hurst, Rees, Orme, & Brown, 1812–14).

SMITH, DONALD, *English Windmills*, Vol. II. Containing a record of the mills in Buckinghamshire, Essex, Hertfordshire, Middlesex and London (Architectural Press, 1932).

TEBBUTT, C. F., *Huntingdonshire Windmills*. Reprinted from Transactions of the Cambridgshire, and Huntingdonshire Archaeological Society, Vol. V, page 433, and Vol. VI, pages 29, 62, 96 and 103 (Mason & Dorman, Ely, 1932).

WAILES, REX, *Windmills in England, a study of their origin, development and future* (Architectural Press, 1948).

BEDFORDSHIRE HISTORICAL RECORD SOCIETY

ELLIOTT, J. STEELE, 'The Windmills of Bedfordshire Past and Present', in *The Publications*, Vol. XIV, and *Survey of Ancient Buildings*, Vol. I (Apsley Guise, 1931).

JUNIOR INSTITUTION OF ENGINEERS, JOURNAL

WAILES, REX, 'The Development of the Windmill', Vol. XLIII, Part 5 (1932).

'Early Windmill Gearing', Vol. XLVI, Part 8 (1936).

'Windmills', Vol. LVII, Part 9 (1947).

NEWCOMEN SOCIETY TRANSACTIONS

BAKER, P. H. J., and WAILES, REX, 'The Windmills of Derbyshire, Leicestershire and Nottinghamshire', Vol. XXXIII (1960–1) and Vol. XXXIX (1961–2).

BURNE, LANCASTER, RUSSELL, JOHN, and WAILES, REX, 'Windmill Sails', Vol. XXVI (1943–5).

CLARK, H. O., and WAILES, REX, 'Brake Wheels and Wallowers', Vol. XXVI (1947–9).

RUSSELL, JOHN, 'Millstones in Wind and Water Mills', Vol. XXIV (1944).

RUSSELL, JOHN, and WAILES, REX, 'Windmills in Kent', Vol. XXIX (1953–5).

TELFORD, THOMAS, 'On Mills', ed. by E. Lancaster Burne, Vol. XVII (1936–7).

TITLEY, ARTHUR, 'Notes on Old Windmills', Vol. III (1922–3).

Bibliography

TITLEY, ARTHUR, and HAINES, D. H., 'A Warwickshire Windmill', Vol. XXVIII (1951–3).

WAILES, REX, 'Brake Wheels and Wallowers', Vol. XXVI (1947–9).
'The Drive to the Stones in Windmills', Vol. XXXI (1957–9).
'Essex Windmills', Vol. XXXI (1957–9).
'Lincolnshire Windmills', Vol. XXVIII (1951–3) and Vol. XXIX (1953–5).
'Norfolk Windmills': Part I, Corn Mills, Vol. XXVI (1947–8).
'Norfolk Windmills': Part II, Drainage and Pumping Mills, Vol. XXX (1955–7).
'Suffolk Windmills'· Part I, Post Mills, Vol. XXII (1941–2).
'Suffolk Windmills': Part II, Tower Mills, Vol. XXIII (1942–3).
'Upright Shafts in Windmills', Vol. XXX (1955–7).
'Windmill Winding Gear', Vol. XXV (1945–7).
'The Windmills of Cambridgeshire', Vol. XXVII (1949–51).
'Windshafts', Vol. XXVI (1947–9).

ST. ALBANS and HERTFORDSHIRE ARCHITECTURAL and ARCHAEOLOGICAL SOCIETY TRANSACTIONS

WESTELL, W. PERCIVAL, 'Sandon Mount, Hertfordshire: Its Site, Excavation and Problems' (1934).

SOCIETY FOR THE PROTECTION OF ANCIENT BUILDINGS

Annual Reports from 1930 et seq.

SUFFOLK INSTITUTE OF ARCHAEOLOGY AND NATURAL HISTORY PROCEEDINGS

WOOLFORD, A, 'Windmills, with Special Reference to those in Suffolk', Vol. XX, Part 2 (1929).

JOHN BARTEL *MILLERUAN 7 1781

CARVING ON THE DOOR OF LAUGHTERTON POST MILL, LINCOLNSHIRE

SCALE OF MILES

0 5 10 20 30 40 50 60

NORTHUMBERLAND

CUMBERLAND   DURHAM

WESTMORLAND

YORKSHIRE

LANCASHIRE

ANGLESEY

CAERNARVON-SHIRE

DENBIGHSHIRE

FLINT

CHESHIRE

DERBYSHIRE

NOTTINGHAM-SHIRE

LINCOLNSHIRE

MERIONETHSHIRE

(FLINT)

STAFFORDSHIRE

LEICESTER-SHIRE

RUT-LAND

NORFOLK

MONTGOMERY-SHIRE

SHROPSHIRE

CARDIGANSHIRE

RADNOR-SHIRE

WORCESTER-SHIRE

WARWICK-SHIRE

NORTHAMPTONSHIRE

HUNTING-DON

SUFFOLK

PEMBROKE-SHIRE

CARMARTHEN-SHIRE

BRECKNOCK-SHIRE

HEREFORD-SHIRE

BEDFORD-SHIRE

CAMBRIDGESHIRE

HERTFORDSHIRE

ESSEX

GLAMORGAN

MONMOUTH-SHIRE

GLOUCESTERSHIRE

OXFORD-SHIRE

BUCKINGHAMSHIRE

MIDDLESEX

LONDON

WILTSHIRE

BERKSHIRE

SURREY

KENT

SOMERSET

HAMPSHIRE

SUSSEX

DEVON

DORSET

CORNWALL

226

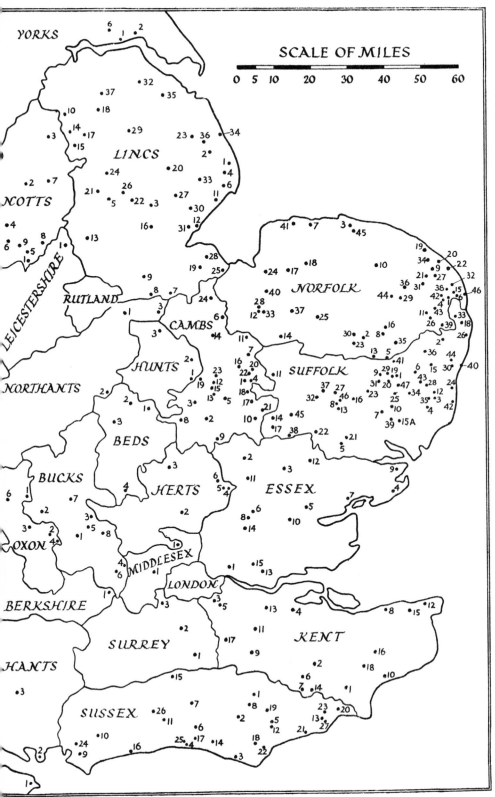

SCALE OF MILES

0 5 10   20   30   40   50   60

MILLS MENTIONED IN THE TEXT

Key to Maps

Anglesey
1 Bryn-dû.
2 Holyhead.

Bedford
1 Eaton Socon.
2 Keysoe.
3 Stevington.
4 Tottenhoe.

Berkshire
1 Windsor.

Bucks
1 Bledlow Ridge.
2 Brill.
3 Cholesbury.
4 Denham.
5 Lacey Green.
6 Slough.
7 Waddesdon.
8 Wycombe Heath (Holmer Green).

Cambridge
1 Adventurers Fen.
2 Barrington.
3 Bourn.
4 Burwell.
5 Cambridge.
6 Christchurch.
7 Ely.
8 Gamlingay.
9 Great Chishill.
10 Linton.
11 Littleport.
12 Long Stanton.
13 Madingley.
14 Manea.
15 Oakington.
16 Stretham.

Cambridge
17 Six Mile Bottom.
18 Swaffham Prior.
19 Swavesey.
20 Soham.
21 West Wratting.
22 Wicken.
23 Willingham.
24 Wisbech.

Cheshire
1 Bidston.
2 Bramhall.
3 Farndon.
4 Gawsworth.
5 Hale.
6 Helsby.

Cornwall
1 Launceston.

Derby
1 Dale Abbey.

Essex
1 Barking.
2 Clavering.
3 Great Bardfield.
4 Great Holland.
5 Hatfield.
6 Little Laver.
7 Layer.
8 Moreton.
9 Ramsey.
10 Roxwell
11 Stansted Mountfitchet.
12 Sible Hedingham.
13 South Ockendon.
14 Toothill.
15 Upminster.

Gloucester
1 Fairford.

Hampshire
1 Bembridge (Isle of Wight).
2 Portsmouth.
3 Owlesbury.

Hertford
1 Arkley.
2 Hatfield.
3 Hitchin.
4 Little Hadham.
5 Much Hadham.
6 Standon.

Huntingdon
1 Holywell.
2 Ramsey.
3 Yaxley.

Kent
1 Appledore.
2 Biddenden.
3 Bromley.
4 Chatham.
5 Chislehurst.
6 Cranbrook.
7 Four Throws.
8 Herne.
9 Hildenborough.
10 Hythe.
11 Kingsdown.
12 Margate.
13 Meopham.
14 Sandhurst.
15 Sarre.
16 Stelling Minnis.
17 Westerham.
18 Willesborough.

Mills mentioned in the Text

Lancashire
1 Clifton.
2 Great Crosby.
3 Liverpool.
4 Preston.
5 Pilling.
6 Rimington.
7 Singleton.
8 Thornton.

Leicester
1 Redmile.

Lincoln
1 Addlethorpe.
2 Alford.
3 Billinghay.
4 Burgh le Marsh.
5 Coleby.
6 Croft.
7 Crowland.
8 Deeping St. James.
9 Dyke.
10 Epworth.
11 Friskney.
12 Freiston.
13 Foston.
14 Gainsborough.
15 Heapham.
16 Heckington.
17 Hemswell.
18 Hibaldstow.
19 Holbeach.
20 Horncastle.
21 Hykeham.
22 Kirkby Green.
23 Legbourne.
24 Lincoln.
25 Lutton.
26 Metheringham.
27 New Bolingbroke.
28 Penny Hill (Holbeach).
29 Rasen.
30 Sibsey.
31 Skirbeck.
32 Stallingborough.
33 Toynton.
34 Trusthorpe.
35 Waltham.
36 Withern.
37 Wrawby.

Middlesex
1 Greenford.

Norfolk
1 Ashtree Farm.
2 Banham.
3 Blakeney.
4 Berney Arms.
5 Billingford.
6 Burgh Castle.
7 Burnham Market.
8 Carleton Rode.
9 Catfield.
10 Cawston.
11 Chedgrave.
12 Denver.
13 Diss.
14 Feltwell.
15 Fleet Dyke.
16 Forncett.
17 Gayton.
18 Great Massingham.
19 Happisburgh.
20 Hickling.
21 Horning.
22 Horsey.
23 Kenninghall.
24 King's Lynn.
25 Little Cressingham.
26 Loddon.
27 Ludham.
28 Nordelph.
29 Norwich.
30 Old Buckenham.
31 Ranworth.
32 Runham.
33 Salters Lode.
34 Stalham.
35 Starston.
36 Sprowston.
37 Stoke Ferry.
38 Stokesby.
39 Toft Monks.
40 Tottenhill.
41 Thornham.
42 Tunstall.
43 Thurlton.
44 Upper Hellesdon.
45 Wiveton.
46 Great Yarmouth.

Northampton
1 Barnack.
2 Bozeat.
3 Eye.

Northumberland
1 Newcastle-upon-Tyne.

Nottingham
1 Costock.
2 Edwinstowe.
3 Blidworth.
4 Hucknall.
5 Keyworth.
6 Kimberley.
7 Laxton.
8 Newton.
9 Strelley.

Oxford
1 Blackthorn.
2 Chinnor.
3 Littleworth (Wheatley).
4 Stokenchurch.
5 Wardington.
6 Weston-on-the-Green.

Pembroke
1 Burton.

Shropshire
1 Ludlow.

Somerset
1 Bishop's Lydeard.
2 Bristol.
3 Ditcheat.
4 Yeovil.

Suffolk
1 Barley Green.
2 Beccles.
3 Benhall.
4 Blaxhall.
5 Boxford.
6 Chippenhall Green.
7 Crowfield.
8 Drinkstone.
9 Eye.
10 Framsden.

Mills mentioned in the Text

Suffolk

11 Freckenham.
12 Friston.
13 Gedding.
14 Great Thurlow.
15 Halesworth.
15A Hasketon.
16 Haughley.
17 Haverhill.
18 Herringfleet.
19 Horham.
20 Huntingfield.
21 Kersey.
22 Long Melford.
23 Mendlesham.
24 Minsmere.
25 Monk Soham.
26 Pakefield.
27 Pakenham.
28 Peasenhall.
29 Redlingfield.
30 Reydon.
31 Rishangles.
32 Rougham.
33 St. Olaves.
34 Saxtead.
35 Snape.
36 South Elmham.
37 Stanton.
38 Stoke-by-Clare.
39 Swilland.
40 Southwold.
41 Syleham.

Suffolk

42 Thorpeness.
43 Ubbeston.
44 Wangford.
45 Wickhambrook.
46 Woolpit.
47 Worlingworth.

Surrey

1 Outwood.
2 Tadworth.
3 Wimbledon.

Sussex

1 Argos Hill (Mayfield).
2 Blackboys.
3 Bishopstone.
4 Brighton.
5 Bodle Street Green.
6 Clayton.
7 Cuckfield.
8 Cross-in-Hand.
9 Fishbourne.
10 Halnaker.
11 Henfield.
12 Herstmonceux.
13 Icklesham.
14 Kingston.
15 Ifield.
16 Littlehampton.
17 Patcham.
18 Polegate.

Sussex

19 Punnetts Town.
20 Rye.
21 Silver Hill.
22 Stone Cross.
23 Udimore.
24 West Ashling.
25 West Blatchington.
26 West Grinstead.
27 Winchelsea.

Warwick

1 Burton Dassett.
2 Chesterton.
3 Compton Wynyates.
4 Coventry.
5 Nuneaton.

Wiltshire

1 Devizes.

Yorkshire

1 Hessle.
2 Hull.
3 Leeds.
4 Rievaulx Abbey.
5 Seaton Ross.
6 Skidby.
7 Skirlaugh.
8 Tollerton.
9 Wakefield.
10 Whitby.

Index

Index

Index

Index

Index

Hickling, Eastfield Mill, 80
  Stubbs Mill, 72, 74
High Ham Mill, 116
High Salvington Mill, 137
Hildenborough, Watts Cross Mill, 106, 127
Hilgay Fen, 80
Hills, of Ashford, millwrights, 101, 123
Hine, R. L., *History of Hitchin*, 171
Hingham, mill moved to Banham, 170
historical recording, 180
History of Corn Milling, Bennett and Elton, 84, 96
Hitchin, removal of mill at, 171
Hockridge water mill, 46
Holbeach, Damgate Mill, 126
  Hurn Mill, 81
  Tindal's eight-sailed mill, 100
hollow post mills, 83, Pl. v
Holmer Green, Wycombe, Heath Mill, 68
Holyhead, Kingsland Mill, 154
Holywell Mill, Pl. xxi
Hondschoote, Deschodt's Mill, 16
Hooper, Captain Stephen, 84, 85, 94, 137
hopper, 16, 18, 26, 131, 132
Hopton Mill, moved from Bardwell, 170
Horham Mill, 25
horizontal mills, 84, 85, Pls. vi, vii
Horncastle, multi-sailed mills at, 103
Horning Mill, 96
Horning Ferry Mill, 109
Hornsby-Ackroyd oil engine, 27
horse, for stones, 16, 131, 132
Horsey Mill, 79
Horsley, the brothers, of Soham, 80, 81
Horton, Mr., of Hythe, 121, 139
Hoxne water mill, 25
Hucknall Mill, 155, 172

Hull, Beverley Road Mill, moved to Trusthorpe, 171
  Subscription Mill, 155
Humphrey, James, of Cranbrook, millwright, 35, 36
Hungerford Bridge, London, sawmill, 144
Hunt, T. B., of Soham, millwright, 52, 63, 68, 80, 81, 116, 170
Huntingfield Mill, 25
husk cupboard, 142
husking barley and oats, 138
Hykeham Moor Mill, 143
Hythe, Black Mill, 139

Iberian Peninsula, mills of the, 104
Icklesham, Hogg Hill Mill, 109
Ickleton Mill, 52
iconography of windmills, 188 *et seq.*
Ifield Mill, 31
Industrial Revolution, effect on windmills, 198
industrial uses of windmills, 144 *et seq.*
Ipswich, 3
Ipswich Journal, 162
Irstead Mill, 83
Isleham Fen Mill, 80
Islington white lead mills, 145, Pl. xxxii
Ison, J. C., of Histon, builder, 169

Jack, 20, 135
jigger, sack, 132
Joycelyn de Brakelond, Chronicles of, 149
jog-scry, 33, 143
Jolesfield Mill, 139
jumper, *see* jog-scry

Keene on Edward Fitzgerald, 178
keep flange, 114
Kegworth Mill, moved from Nottingham Forest, 172
Kelly, Michael, *A Friend in Need*, 167
Kenilworth, Lord, 81

237

Index

Index

Index

Index

243

Index

Index

Index